3/20

St. Paul Lutheran Church
ALTA, IOWA

The Children's Hymnal

Howard Bowen

Young David and his harp

The Children's Hymnal

*Singing and making melody
in your heart to the Lord*
— EPHESIANS 5:19

CONCORDIA PUBLISHING HOUSE — SAINT LOUIS, MISSOURI

The
Children's
Hymnal

Library of Congress Catalog Card Number M 55-1001

MANUFACTURED IN THE UNITED STATES OF AMERICA

Preface

The Children's Hymnal is, as the name indicates, a compilation of hymns and spiritual songs particularly appropriate for the training and edification of older children. The book also includes twelve orders of service, a careful selection of Psalms and Scripture readings, prayers for various occasions written in the language of children, a group of collects, Luther's Small Catechism, and several helpful indexes.

When the committee began its work, it agreed upon the following criteria for a selection of hymns for older children of the Church: (1) The concepts must be thoroughly in harmony with the Bible, and the doctrines presented ought to be properly balanced. (2) The words and ideas are to fit the understanding of the children for whom the book is intended, chiefly children between the ages of 8 and 14. (3) The hymns are to be good poetry. Triteness and sentimentality are to be avoided.

In judging the value of tunes to be selected, the committee applied these principles: (1) The tunes are to be diatonic and chordal in character, and they should be musically sound and inspiring. (2) The range is not to exceed a tenth, and is to be kept within an octave if possible. (3) The tunes are to harmonize with the spirit of the texts with which they are combined.

The committee was aware of the great danger of stressing music of the moment and neglecting the great hymns which Christians have sung throughout the centuries. Church leaders and Christian parents have the responsibility and duty of giving to their children the choicest treasures of the Church for the worship of God and are not to substitute what is trite and mediocre, and sometimes even false, for that which is pure, wholesome, instructive, and uplifting. St. Paul said, "Prove all things; hold fast that which is good."

On the other hand, many letters from pastors, teachers, and workers with children emphasized strongly the fact that much of what has been called the classical heritage of the Church can be understood only by adults. Church school leaders, concerned first of all with the spiritual life of the children, have rightly demanded that the materials for children's worship be suited to the comprehension of the child.

The committee spent several years in consulting hymnals and in meeting almost weekly. It has attempted to prepare for the schools and homes of the Church a hymnal which is instructive, deeply spiritual, and of lasting value. At the same time, great pains were taken to make the book thoroughly suitable for children.

About two-thirds of the book consists of well-known hymns of the Church, since one of the purposes of a Christian school is to train the children for worship in the church services. These hymns were carefully edited for simplicity. Many of the simpler chorales, thoroughly Christian and churchly, have been included.

Also some of the so-called lighter hymns have been chosen because they present the Gospel of God's love in Christ in a simple and easily singable manner and express a childlike trust in God's forgiveness and care.

Almost one-third of the hymn section consists of relatively new hymns, many especially prepared for children. Church school leaders are urged to give due consideration also to the hymns with which the children are not acquainted. Frequent use of unknown hymns will strengthen the children in their worship life.

No doubt many individuals will regret the omission of certain favorite hymns and tunes. Some will want more chorales; others more hymns of a lighter quality. Limitations of space and the desire for a balanced content required careful choosing. The committee's original selection consisted of more than twice the number finally agreed upon.

In a few instances a new musical setting for familiar words is being offered in spite of the fact that this innovation may disturb some people for a time. These changes, however, were made only when the committee was thoroughly convinced that a much better melody could be provided than the one currently in use. Some of these combinations already have found favor in certain branches of the Church. Perhaps the most striking example of this improvement is the melodic and delightful setting by Ralph Vaughan Williams for the hymn "God Be with You till We Meet Again."

Whenever a popular hymn tune was musically acceptable, it was retained; however, a second tune was added to a few hymns which the committee believed should be improved. A good example of this addition of a second tune is the beautifully descriptive tune "Aberystwyth" for the hymn "Jesus, Lover of My Soul."

Some of the hymns are arranged under special headings, since many of these can properly be used only in certain seasons or with specific themes. A large number, however, have been placed into a "General" section so as not to restrict their use.

The book is presented with the hope that it may help to rear a generation of children who will gladly sing the praises of Him who has called them out of darkness into His marvelous light. "Sing forth the honor of His name; make His praise glorious" (Psalm 66:2).

HARRY J. BERNTHAL
ALLAN H. JAHSMANN
EDWARD W. KLAMMER
ARNOLD C. MUELLER

Acknowledgments

The committee is grateful for the many original hymns submitted for consideration, and for the permissions to use selected material. Specific acknowledgments are given to copyright holders in the footnotes. Authors and composers are indicated at the top of each hymn. If any hymns have been included without the necessary permission, credit will gladly be given in future editions. Several of the hymns are from *Our Songs of Praise*, edited by Edward W. Klammer.

A special word of thanks is due the members of the Committee on Hymnology and Liturgics, whose advice and assistance in this project were of great benefit. The committee also was guided by the many responses to the publication of the tentative selection of hymns. Prof. Carl Halter, an advisory member of the committee, read the completed manuscript thoughtfully and suggested a number of improvements.

Contents

The Hymns

Resources for Worship

Indexes

ix

Illustrations

The *Children's Hymnal* is strikingly rich in Christian symbolism and other illustrations. Christian symbols, like Christian hymns, are vehicles of the Christian faith and a part of the precious heritage of the Christian Church. To appreciate symbols, one must understand their meaning. Following is a brief explanation of some of the traditional symbols used in this hymnal. The thoughtful illustrations so nobly designed are by Evelyn Ortlepp. They not only interpret and inspire but also give to the book a fitting devotional tone. The original painting of young David, the sweet singer of Israel, which appears as a frontispiece in four colors, is by Howard Bowen. The interesting cover design is by Otto Keisker. All three are well-known St. Louis artists. The numbers below refer to hymns or pages.

Hymns 1 to 300

1. The herald's trumpet announces the coming of the promised Savior.
8. The Star in the East signals the birth of our King.
11. The Christmas tree points to Jesus, the Bright and Morning Star.
15. The faithful of all the world sing the Christ-Child's praises.
30. Wise Men came from the East to worship Him.
32. Jesus gained the crown of victory ⟨and⟩ glory through the cross and crown of suffering.
36. The "Agnus Dei" or "Lamb of God" symbol reminds us that the suffering Jesus was the Lamb of God. He bears a victory banner attached to a staff with a cross at its tip.
43. The naked cross and the empty tomb symbolize Christ's victory over death.
51. The rising sun represents the Resurrection morning and the dawn of new life that burst forth from the tomb.
59. The descending dove is the most common symbol of the Holy Spirit.
61. The triangle and the so-called trefoil, a three-leaved herb, remind us that the Holy Spirit is one of the Persons of the Holy Trinity.
65. The all-seeing eye is a symbol of God the Father; the lamb, of the Son; and the dove, of the Holy Spirit. The anchor represents our hope in the Triune God of the Bible.
69. The interwoven circles are another symbol of the Trinity.
72. The Wartburg and the advancing crusaders represent the work of Luther and the Reformation.
75. The door of one's heart is opened by the Good Shepherd, who gave His life on the cross.

The
Hymns

Oh, sing unto the Lord a new song:
For He hath done marvelous things.

— PSALM 98:1

1

Hark the Glad Sound! The Savior Comes

Chesterfield—C. M.

Philip Doddridge, 1735, cento

Thomas Haweis, 1792

1 Hark the glad sound! The Sav - ior comes, The Sav - ior prom -ised long; Let ev - 'ry heart pre - pare a throne And ev - 'ry voice a song.

2
He comes the broken heart to bind,
The bleeding soul to cure,
And with the treasures of His grace
T' enrich the humble poor.

3
Our glad hosannas, Prince of Peace,
Thy welcome shall proclaim
And heaven's eternal arches ring
With Thy beloved name.

Hosanna Now Through Advent

Maria ist geboren—7. 6. 7. 6.

Claudia F. Hernaman, 1838-1898

Coeln (Brachel, 1623)
Harm. by Charles Wood

1 Ho - san - na now through Ad - vent With lov - ing hearts we sing, For Je - sus Christ is com - ing To be His chil - dren's King.

2
Hosanna! Blessed Jesus,
 Come in our hearts to dwell,
And let our lives and voices
 Thy praise and glory tell.

3
For we who sing Hosanna
 Must like our Savior be,
In gentleness and meekness,
 In love and purity.

4
Hosanna! Let this welcome
 Ring out from ev'ry heart;
Draw nigh to us, O Jesus,
 And nevermore depart.

5
So when we see Thee coming
 With angels in the sky,
Hosanna! loud Hosanna!
 Shall be Thy children's cry.

On Jordan's Bank the Baptist's Cry

Puer nobis nascitur—L. M.

Charles Coffin, 1736, ab.
St. 1-3, tr., John Chandler, 1837
St. 4, 5, tr., unknown

"Musae Sioniae," VI, 1609

1 On Jor-dan's bank the Bap-tist's cry An-nounc-es that the Lord is nigh; Come, then, and heark-en, for he brings Glad ti-dings from the King of Kings.

2

Then cleansed be ev'ry Christian breast
And furnished for so great a Guest.
Yea, let us each our hearts prepare
For Christ to come and enter there.

3

For Thou art our Salvation, Lord,
Our Refuge, and our great Reward.
Without Thy grace our souls must fade
And wither like a flow'r decayed.

4

Lay on the sick Thy healing hand
And make the fallen strong to stand;
Show us the glory of Thy face
Till beauty springs in every place.

5

All praise, eternal Son, to Thee
Whose advent sets Thy people free,
Whom, with the Father, we adore,
And Holy Ghost forevermore.

Lift Up Your Heads, Ye Mighty Gates

First Tune—Macht hoch die Tür—8. 8. 8. 8. 8. 8. 6. 6.

Georg Weissel, 1642
Tr., Catherine Winkworth, 1855, alt.

August Lemke, 1849

1 Lift up your heads, ye might-y gates! Be-hold, the King of Glo-ry waits;

The King of kings is draw-ing near, The Sav-ior of the world is here.

Life and sal-va-tion He doth bring, Where-fore re-joice and glad-ly sing:

We praise Thee, Fa-ther, now, Cre-a-tor, wise art Thou!

2
Oh, blest the land, the city blest,
Where Christ the Ruler is confessed!
O happy hearts and happy homes
To whom this King in triumph comes!
The cloudless Sun of joy He is,
Who bringeth pure delight and bliss.
We praise Thee, Spirit, now,
Our Comforter art Thou!

3
Redeemer, come! I open wide
My heart to Thee; here, Lord, abide!
Let me Thine inner presence feel,
Thy grace and love in me reveal;
Thy Holy Spirit guide us on
Until our glorious goal is won.
Eternal praise and fame
We offer to Thy name.

Lift Up Your Heads, Ye Mighty Gates

Second Tune—Macht hoch die Tuer—8. 8. 8. 8. 8. 8. 6. 6.

Georg Weissel, 1642
Tr., Catherine Winkworth, 1855, alt.

Johann A. Freylinghausen, 1704

1 Lift up your heads, ye might-y gates! Be-hold, the King of Glo-ry waits; The King of Kings is draw-ing near, The Sav-ior of the world is here. Life and sal-va-tion He doth bring, Where-fore re-joice and glad-ly sing: We praise Thee, Fa-ther, now, Cre-a-tor, wise art Thou!

Oh, Come, Oh, Come, Emmanuel

Veni, Emmanuel—8. 8. 8. 8. 8. 8.

Latin author unknown, c. 1100
Tr., John M. Neale, 1851, 1859, ab.

Plain-song melody, c. 1200
Adapted by Thomas Helmore, 1854

1 Oh, come, oh, come, Em - man - u - el, And ran-som cap - tive Is - ra - el, That mourns in lone - ly ex - ile here Un - til the Son of God ap-pear. Re - joice! Re - joice! Em-man - u - el Shall come to thee, O Is - ra - el!

Tune arrangement by Canon Winfred Douglas. Used by permission of The Church Pension Fund.

2

Oh, come, Thou Rod of Jesse, free
Thine own from Satan's tyranny;
From depths of hell Thy people save,
And give them vict'ry o'er the grave.
Rejoice! Rejoice! Emmanuel
Shall come to thee, O Israel.

3

Oh, come, Thou Key of David, come
And open wide our heav'nly home;
Make safe the way that leads on high,
And close the path to misery.
Rejoice! Rejoice! Emmanuel
Shall come to thee, O Israel.

6

Come, Jesus, Holy Child, to Me
Vom Himmel hoch—L. M.

Hofgesangbuch, Leipzig, 1672
Tr., Paul Z. Strodach, 1928

"Geistliche Lieder"
Leipzig, 1539

1 Come, Je-sus, ho-ly Child, to me, Close
tight my heart to all but Thee, And with Thy Ho-ly
Spir-it's grace Make me, dear Lord, Thy dwell-ing place.

2

And leave me not, Thou heav'nly
    Guest,
But in Thy favor let me rest;
With Thee alone will always be
All joy and blessedness for me.

3

With joy and love I wait for Thee
To come with Thy good gifts to me.
Stay close to me all through my days;
Then let me sing in heav'n Thy
    praise.

Come, Thou Long-Expected Jesus

Hyfrydol—8. 7. 8. 7. D.

Charles Wesley, 1744

Rowland H. Prichard, †1887, alt.

1 Come, Thou long-ex-pect-ed Je-sus, Born to set Thy peo-ple free;

From our fears and sins re-lease us; Let us find our rest in Thee.

Is-rael's Strength and Con - so - la-tion, Hope of all the earth Thou art,

Dear De - sire of ev -'ry na-tion, Joy of ev -'ry long-ing heart.

2
Born Thy people to deliver;
  Born a Child, and yet a King;
Born to reign in us forever,
  Now Thy gracious kingdom bring.
By Thine own eternal Spirit
  Rule in all our hearts alone;
By Thine all-sufficient merit
  Raise us to Thy glorious throne.

Silent Night! Holy Night!

Stille Nacht—Irregular

Joseph Mohr, 1818
Tr., unknown

Franz Gruber, 1818

1 Si - lent night! Ho - ly night! All is calm, all is bright,

Round yon Vir - gin Moth-er and Child. Ho - ly In -fant, so

ten-der and mild, Sleep in heav-en-ly peace, Sleep in heav-en-ly peace.

2
Silent night! Holy night!
Shepherds quake at the sight;
Glories stream from heaven afar,
Heav'nly hosts sing, Alleluia,
Christ, the Savior is born!
Christ, the Savior is born!

3
Silent night! Holy night!
Son of God, love's pure light
Radiant beams from Thy holy face,
With the dawn of redeeming grace,
Jesus, Lord, at Thy birth,
Jesus, Lord at Thy birth.

Joy to the World, the Lord Is Come

Antioch—C. M.

Isaac Watts, 1719

Georg F. Haendel, 1742, arr.

1 Joy to the world, the Lord is come! Let earth receive her King; Let ev-'ry heart pre-pare Him room And heav'n and na-ture sing, And heav'n and na-ture sing, And heav'n, and heav'n and na-ture sing.

2

Joy to the earth, the Savior reigns!
Let men their songs employ,
While fields and floods, rocks, hills,
and plains
Repeat the sounding joy.

3

No more let sins and sorrows grow
Nor thorns infest the ground;
He comes to make His blessings flow
Far as the curse is found.

4

He rules the world with truth and
grace
And makes the nations prove
The glories of His righteousness
And wonders of His love.

All My Heart This Day Rejoices

Froehlich soll mein Herze—8. 3. 3. 6. 8. 3. 3. 6.

Paul Gerhardt, 1653
Tr., Catherine Winkworth, 1858, alt., cento

Johann Crueger, 1653

1 All my heart this day re-joic-es As I hear Far and near Sweet-est an-gel voic-es. "Christ is born," their choirs are sing-ing Till the air Ev-'ry-where Now with joy is ring-ing.

2
Hark! a voice from yonder manger,
  Soft and sweet, Doth entreat:
"Flee from woe and danger.
  Brethren, from all ills that grieve
    you
You are freed; All you need
  I will surely give you."

3
Come, then, banish all your sadness,
  One and all, Great and small,
Come with songs of gladness.
  Love Him who with love is
    glowing;
Hail the Star Near and far
  Light and joy bestowing.

4
Let me in my arms receive Thee;
  On Thy breast Let me rest,
Savior, ne'er to leave Thee.
  Since Thou hast Thyself presented
Now to me, I shall be
  Evermore contented.

11

From Heaven Above to Earth I Come

Vom Himmel hoch—L. M.

Martin Luther, 1535
Tr., Catherine Winkworth, 1855, alt., cento

"Geistliche Lieder"
Leipzig, 1539

1 "From heav'n a-bove to earth I come To bear good news to ev-'ry home;

Glad ti-dings of great joy I bring, Where-of I now will say and sing:

2
"To you this night is born a Child
Of Mary, chosen virgin mild;
This little Child, of lowly birth,
Shall be the Joy of all the earth.

3
"This is the Christ, our God and
Lord,
Who in all need shall aid afford;
He will Himself your Savior be
From all your sins to set you free.

4
Welcome to earth, Thou noble Guest,
Through whom the sinful world is
blest!
Thou com'st to share my misery;
What thanks shall I return to Thee?

5
Ah, dearest Jesus, holy Child,
Make Thee a bed, soft, undefiled,
Within my heart, that it may be
A quiet chamber kept for Thee.

6
My heart for very joy doth leap,
My lips no more can silence keep;
I, too, must sing with joyful tongue
That sweetest ancient cradle song:

7
Glory to God in highest heaven,
Who unto us His Son hath given!
While angels sing with pious mirth
A glad new year to all the earth.

Praise God the Lord, Ye Sons of Men

Lobt Gott, ihr Christen—C. M.

Nikolaus Herman, 1560
Tr., August Crull, †1923, alt., cento

Nikolaus Herman, 1554

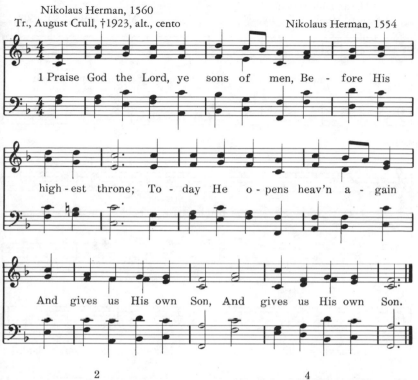

1 Praise God the Lord, ye sons of men, Be - fore His high - est throne; To - day He o - pens heav'n a - gain And gives us His own Son, And gives us His own Son.

2
He leaves His heav'nly Father's throne,
 Is born an Infant small,
And in a manger, poor and lone,
 Lies in a humble stall.

3
He nestles at His mother's breast,
 Receives her tender care,
Whom angels hail with joy most blest,
 King David's royal Heir.

4
He serves that I a lord may be;
 A great exchange indeed!
Could Jesus' love do more for me
 To help me in my need?

5
He opens us again the door
 Of Paradise today;
The angel guards the gate no more.
 ᵗTo God our thanks we pay.

To Shepherds as They Watched by Night

Puer nobis nascitur—L. M.

Martin Luther, 1543
Tr., Richard Massie, 1854, alt., ab.

"Musae Sioniae," VI, 1609

1 To shep-herds as they watched by night Ap - peared a host of an - gels bright; Be - hold the ten - der Babe, they said, In yon - der low - ly man - ger laid.

2

At Bethlehem, in David's town,
As Micah did of old make known;
'Tis Jesus Christ, your Lord and King,
Who doth to all salvation bring.

3

Oh, then rejoice that through His Son
God is with sinners now at one;
Made like yourselves of flesh and
blood,
Your brother is th' eternal God.

4

What harm can sin and death then
do?
The true God now abides with you.
Let hell and Satan rage and chafe,
Christ is your Brother, ye are safe.

A Great and Mighty Wonder

Es ist ein' Ros'—7. 6. 7. 6. 6. 7. 6.

St. Germanus, †734
Tr., John M. Neale, 1862, alt., ab.

"Alte geistliche Kirchengesäng"
Cologne, 1599

1 A great and might-y won-der, A full and ho-ly cure: The Vir-gin bears the In-fant With vir-gin hon-or pure! Re-peat the hymn a-gain: "To God on high be glo-ry And peace on earth to men!"

2
The Word becomes incarnate
And yet remains on high,
And cherubim sing anthems
To shepherds from the sky.
Repeat the hymn again:
"To God on high be glory
And peace on earth to men!"

3
While thus they sing your Monarch,
Those bright angelic bands,
Rejoice, ye vales and mountains,
Ye oceans, clap your hands.
Repeat the hymn again:
"To God on high be glory
And peace on earth to men!"

4
Since all He comes to ransom,
By all be He adored,
The Infant born in Bethl'em,
The Savior and the Lord.
Repeat the hymn again:
"To God on high be glory
And peace on earth to men!"

Oh, Come, All Ye Faithful

Adeste, fideles—Irregular

Author unknown, 18th century
Tr., Edward Caswall and
Philip Schaff, 1849, 1870, cento

"Cantus Diversi," 1751

1 Oh, come, all ye faith-ful, tri-um-phant-ly sing;

Come, see in the man-ger our Sav-ior and King!

To Beth-le-hem has-ten with joy-ful ac-cord;

Oh, come, let us a-dore Him, Oh, come, let us a-dore Him,

Oh, come, let us a - dore Him, Christ the Lord!

2

True Son of the Father, He comes from the skies;
To be born of a virgin He doth not despise.
To Bethlehem hasten with joyful accord;
Oh, come, let us adore Him, Christ the Lord!

3

Hark, hark, to the angels all singing in heaven:
"To God in the highest all glory be given!"
To Bethlehem hasten with joyful accord;
Oh, come, let us adore Him, Christ the Lord!

4

To Thee, then, O Jesus, this day of Thy birth
Be glory and honor through heaven and earth,
True Godhead incarnate, omnipotent Word!
Oh, come, let us adore Him, Christ the Lord!

O Little Town of Bethlehem

St. Louis—8. 6. 4. 4. 6. 7. 6. 4. 4. 6.

Phillips Brooks, 1868, ab.   Lewis H. Redner, 1868

1 O lit-tle town of Beth-le-hem, How still we see thee lie!

A - bove thy deep And dream-less sleep The si - lent stars go by;

Yet in thy dark-ness shin - eth The ev - er - last-ing Light;

The hopes and fears Of all the years Are met in thee to - night.

2

For Christ is born of Mary,
   And gathered all above,
While mortals sleep, The angels keep
   Their watch of wond'ring love.
O morning stars, together
   Proclaim the holy birth,
And praises sing To God, the King,
   And peace to men on earth.

3

How silently, how silently,
   The wondrous Gift is giv'n!
So God imparts To human hearts
   The blessings of His heav'n.
No ear may hear His coming,
   But in this world of sin,
Where meek souls will Receive Him
      still,
   The dear Christ enters in.

4

O holy Child of Bethlehem,
  Descend to us, we pray;
Cast out our sin, And enter in,
  Be born in us today.

We hear the Christmas angels
  The great glad tidings tell:
Oh, come to us, Abide with us,
  Our Lord Immanuel!

17

Little Children, Wake and Listen

Polish Melody—8. 8. 8. 8. 4.

Adapted by John Cozens
from an anonymous poem

Harm. by John Cozens

1 Lit - tle chil - dren, wake and lis - ten, While the stars in heav-en glis - ten, Hear an - gel - ic voic - es swell - ing, Such a won-drous tale they're tell-ing: "Je - sus is born!"

2

Words to bring us greater gladness,
Words to chase away our sadness,
Christ has left His throne of glory,
Well might angels tell the story:
  "Jesus is born!"

3

Let me kneel, my Lord, before Thee,
Let me, for Thy love, adore Thee,
Like the angels o'er the meadows,
May I sing through earthly shadows:
  "Jesus is born!"

From *Uncommon Christmas Carols.* Copyright 1941 by Hall & McCreary Co.
Used by permission.

Hark! the Herald Angels Sing

Mendelssohn—7. 7. 7. 7. D., with Refrain

Charles Wesley, 1739, et al.   Felix Mendelssohn, 1840, ad.

1 Hark! the her - ald an - gels sing, "Glo - ry to the
new - born King; Peace on earth and mer - cy mild,
God and sin - ners rec - on - ciled!" Joy - ful, all ye
na - tions, rise, Join the tri - umph of the skies;
With th' an - gel - ic host pro-claim, "Christ is born in Beth-le-hem!"

Hark! the her-ald an-gels sing, "Glo-ry to the new-born King!"

2

Christ, by highest heav'n adored,
Christ, the everlasting Lord,
Late in time behold Him come,
Offspring of a virgin's womb.
Veiled in flesh the Godhead see,
Hail th' incarnate Deity!
Pleased as Man with man to dwell;
Jesus, our Immanuel!
Hark! the herald angels sing,
"Glory to the newborn King!"

3

Hail, the heav'nly Prince of Peace!
Hail, the Sun of Righteousness!
Light and life to all He brings,
Ris'n with healing in His wings.
Mild He leaves His throne on high,
Born that man no more may die;
Born to raise the sons of earth;
Born to give them second birth.
Hark! the herald angels sing,
"Glory to the newborn King!"

4

Come, Desire of nations, come,
Fix in us Thy humble home;
Oh, to all Thyself impart,
Formed in each believing heart!
Hark! the herald angels sing,
"Glory to the newborn King;
Peace on earth and mercy mild,
God and sinners reconciled!"
Hark! the herald angels sing,
"Glory to the newborn King!"

Unto Us a Boy Is Born

Omega and Alpha—7. 6. 7. 7.

15th-century German carol
Tr., Percy Dearmer, 1867-1936

From Piae Cantiones, 1582
Arr. by Geoffrey Shaw

1 Un - to us a Boy is born! King of all cre - a - tion, Came He to a world for - lorn, The Lord of ev - 'ry na - tion.

2
Cradled in a stall was He
  With sleepy cows and asses;
But the very beasts could see
  That He all men surpasses.

3
Herod then with fear was filled:
  "A Prince," he said, "in Jewry!"
All the little boys he killed
  At Bethl'em in his fury.

4
Now may Mary's Son, who came
  So long ago to love us,
Lead us all with hearts aflame
  Unto the joys above us.

5
He the Source and He the End!
  Let the organ thunder,
While our happy voices rend
  The joyful air asunder!

In Bethlehem, the Lowly

Dutch Carol—Irregular

Coelner Psalter, 1638
Tr., composite

Traditional, 1638

1 In Beth-le-hem, the low-ly, a Child was born this day; Him will I wor-ship on-ly, While on this earth I stay. Oh,—yes! Oh,—yes! A Child was born this day.

2
And while in awe I ponder
The mystery divine,
My heart is lost in wonder
That Christ is also mine.

3
How can we, dearest Jesus,
Repay Thy wondrous love
Wherein Thou cam'st to save us
From Thy great throne above?

4
My life, my all I bring Thee,
Oh, lend me, I implore,
Thy grace to serve and love Thee
Now and forevermore.

Angels We Have Heard on High

Gloria—7. 7. 7. 7, with Refrain

Traditional French carol

French carol melody

1 An-gels we have heard on high, Sweet-ly sing-ing o'er the plains;

And the moun-tains in re - ply Ech - o - ing their joy - ous strains.

Glo - - - - - - - - - ri - a

in ex - cel - sis De - o, Glo - - - - -

- - - - ri - a in ex - cel - sis De - o.

2

Shepherds, why this jubilee?
  Why these songs of happy cheer?
What great brightness did you see?
  What glad tidings did you hear?

Refrain:

3

Come to Bethlehem, and see
  Him whose birth the angels sing;
Come, adore on bended knee
  Christ, the Lord, the newborn King.

Refrain:

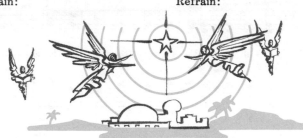

22

Let Us All with Gladsome Voice

Lasst uns alle—7. 6. 7. 6. Trochaic

Author unknown, 1632
Tr., Catherine Winkworth, 1863, alt.

"Gesangbuch, Ander Teil"
Dresden, 1632

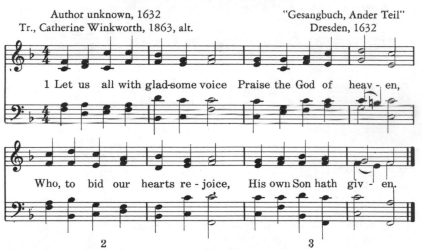

1 Let us all with gladsome voice Praise the God of heav-en,

Who, to bid our hearts re-joice, His own Son hath giv-en.

2

To this vale of tears He comes,
Here to serve in sadness,
That with Him in heav'n's fair homes
We may reign in gladness.

3

We are rich, for He was poor;
Is not this a wonder?
Therefore praise God evermore
Here on earth and yonder.

4

O Lord Christ, our Savior dear,
Be Thou ever near us.
Grant us now a glad new year.
Amen, Jesus, hear us!

23

Once in Royal David's City

Irby—8. 7. 8. 7. 8. 8.

Cecil Frances Alexander, 1823-1895 — Henry John Gauntlett, 1805-1876

1 Once in roy-al Da-vid's cit-y Stood a low-ly cat-tle shed,
Where a moth-er laid her Ba-by In a man-ger for His bed;
Ma-ry was that moth-er mild, Je-sus Christ, her lit-tle Child.

2

He came down to earth from heaven
  Who is God and Lord of all,
And His shelter was a stable,
  And His cradle was a stall;
With the poor and mean and lowly
Lived on earth our Savior holy.

3

And our eyes at last shall see Him,
  Through His own redeeming love;
For that Child so dear and gentle
  Is our Lord in heaven above,
And He leads His children on
To the place where He is gone.

On Christmas Night

Sussex Carol—8. 8. 8. 8.

Traditional

Arr. by Ralph Vaughan Williams, b. 1872

1 On Christ-mas night all Chris-tians sing For all the news the an - gels bring. On Christ-mas night all Chris-tians sing For all the news the an - gels bring, News of great joy, news of great mirth, News of our ho - ly Sav-ior's birth!

2
When sin departs before His grace,
Then life and health come in its place,
When sin departs before His grace,
Then life and health come in its place,
Angels and men full well may sing;
All is due to our newborn King.

3
From out of darkness we have light
Which makes the angels sing this
    night;
From out of darkness we have light
Which makes the angels sing this
    night:
"Glory to God and peace to men,
Now and forevermore. Amen."

25

Oh, Come, All Ye Children

Ihr Kinderlein, kommet—11. 11. 11. 11.

Christian v. Schmid, Tr. anon.   Johann Abraham Peter Schulz, 1747-1800

1 Oh, come, all ye chil-dren, oh, come, one and all,

To Beth-le-hem haste, to the man-ger so small,

God's Son for a gift has been sent you this

night To be your Re-deem-er, your Joy and De-light.

2

He's born in a stable for you and for
  me,
Draw near by the bright gleaming
  starlight to see,
In swaddling clothes lying, so meek
  and so mild,
And purer than angels, the heavenly
  Child.

3

See Mary and Joseph with love-beam-
  ing eyes
Are gazing upon the rude bed where
  He lies,
The shepherds are kneeling, with
  hearts full of love,
While angels sing loud hallelujahs
  above.

4

Kneel down and adore Him with
  shepherds today,
Lift up little hands now, and praise
  Him as they;
Rejoice that a Savior from sin you
  can boast,
And join in the song of the heavenly
  host.

5

Dear Christ Child, what gifts can we
  children bestow
By which our affection and gladness
  to show?
No riches and treasures of value can
  be,
But hearts that believe are accepted
  with Thee.

6

Our hearts, then, to Thee we will
  offer today,
We offer them gladly, accept them,
  we pray,
And make them so spotless and pure
  that we may
Abide in Thy presence in heaven for
  aye.

26

In the Bleak Midwinter

Cranham—Irregular

Christina G. Rossetti, 1830-1894   Gustav Holst, 1874-1935

1 In the bleak mid-win-ter, Frost-y wind made moan,
2 Our God, heav'n can-not hold Him, Nor earth sus-tain;
3 An-gels and arch-an-gels May have gath-ered there,
4 What can I give Him, Poor as I am?

Earth stood hard as i - ron, Wa-ter like a stone;
Heav'n and earth shall flee a-way When He comes to reign;
Cher - u - bim and ser - a - phim Throng - èd the air;
If I were a shep - herd, I would bring a lamb;

Snow had fal-len, snow on snow, Snow on snow,
In the bleak mid - win - ter A sta-ble place suf-ficed The
But His moth-er on - ly, In her maid-en bliss,
If I were a wise man, I would do my part; Yet

In the bleak mid - win - ter, Long a - go.
Lord God Al - might-y, Je - sus Christ.
Wor-shiped the Be - lov - ed With a kiss.
what I can I give Him — Give my heart.

Words from The Poetical Works of Rosetti, The Macmillan Company. Used by permission. Music used by permission of Gustav Holst.

Rejoice and Be Merry

Dorset Carol—11.11.11.11.

A Dorset carol

Harm. by Martin Shaw, 1876-

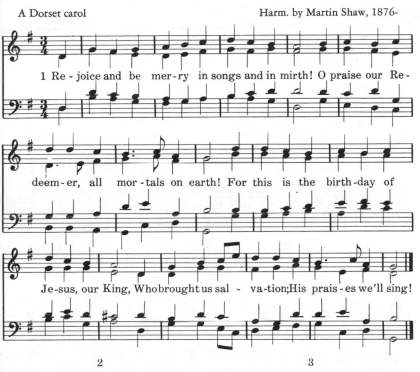

1 Re - joice and be mer-ry in songs and in mirth! O praise our Re-deem-er, all mor-tals on earth! For this is the birth-day of Je-sus, our King, Who brought us sal - va-tion; His prais-es we'll sing!

2

A heavenly vision appeared in the
    sky;
Vast numbers of angels the shepherds
    did spy,
Proclaiming the birthday of Jesus,
    our King,
Who brought us salvation—His
    praises we'll sing!

3

Likewise a bright star in the sky did
    appear
Which led the Wise Men from the
    East to draw near;
They found the Messiah, sweet Jesus,
    our King,
Who brought us salvation—His
    praises we'll sing!

4

And when they were come, they
    their treasures unfold
And unto Him offered myrrh, incense,
    and gold.
So blessed forever be Jesus, our King,
Who brought us salvation—His
    praises we'll sing!

28

The Snow Lay on the Ground

Venite, adoremus—Irregular, with Refrain

Traditional carol, alt.

Traditional melody
Harm. by Leo Sowerby, 1941

1 The snow lay on the ground, The stars shone bright, When

Christ our Lord was born On Christ - mas night.

Ve - ni - te, ad - o - re - mus Do - mi - num; Ve-

ni - te, ad - o - re - mus Do - mi - num.

Refrain (after each stanza)

Ve - ni - te, ad - o - re - mus Do - mi - num, Ve-

ni - te, ad - o - re - mus Do - mi - num.

2

'Twas Mary, virgin mild,
  Of Mother Anne,
That brought into this world
  The God made man.
She laid Him in a stall
  At Bethlehem;
The ass and oxen shared
  The roof with them.

Refrain.

3

And Joseph, too, was by
  To tend the Child,
To guard Him and protect
  His mother mild.
The angels hovered round
  And sang this song,
Venite, adoremus
  Dominum.

Refrain.

4

And thus that manger poor
  Became a throne;
For He whom Mary bore
  Was God the Son.
Oh, come, then, let us join
  The heav'nly host,
To praise the Father, Son,
  And Holy Ghost.

Refrain.

See also:
  Away in a Manger
  As Each Happy Christmas
  A Little Child on the Earth Has Been Born
  Come Ye All to Bethlehem

29

The Star Proclaims the King Is Here

Wo Gott zum Haus—L. M.

Coelius Sedulius, c. 450
Tr., John M. Neale, 1852, alt.

"Geistliche Lieder"
Wittenberg, 1535

1 The star pro-claims the King is here; But, Her-od, why this sense-less fear? He takes no realms of earth a-way Who gives the realms of heav'n-ly day.

2

The wiser Magi see from far
And follow on His guiding star;
And led by light, to light they press
And by their gifts their God confess.

3

Within the Jordan's crystal flood
In meekness stands the Lamb of God
And, sinless, sanctifies the wave,
Mankind from sin to cleanse and save.

4

At Cana first His power is shown;
His might the blushing waters own
And, changing as He speaks the word,
Flow wine, obedient to their Lord.

5

All glory, Jesus, be to Thee
For this Thy glad epiphany;
Whom with the Father we adore
And Holy Ghost forevermore.

As with Gladness Men of Old

Dix—7. 7. 7. 7. 7. 7.

William C. Dix, 1860, ab.

Konrad Kocher, 1838

1 As with glad-ness men of old Did the guid-ing star be-hold;

As with joy they hailed its light, Lead-ing on-ward, beam-ing bright,

So, most gra-cious Lord, may we Ev-er-more be led by Thee!

2
As with joyful steps they sped,
Savior, to Thy lowly bed,
There to bend the knee before
Thee whom heav'n and earth adore,
So may we with willing feet
Ever seek Thy mercy seat!

3
As they offered gifts most rare
At Thy cradle, rude and bare,
So may we with holy joy,
Pure and free from sin's alloy,
All our costliest treasures bring,
Christ, to Thee, our heav'nly King!

4
Holy Jesus, every day
Keep us in the narrow way;
And, when earthly things are past,
Bring our ransomed souls at last
Where they need no star to guide,
Where no clouds Thy glory hide.

Brightest and Best of the Sons of the Morning

Morning Star—11. 10. 11. 10.

Reginald Heber, 1811   James P. Harding, 1892

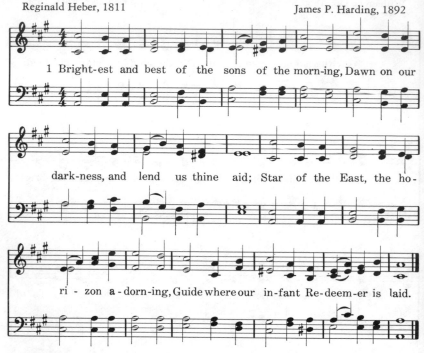

1 Bright-est and best of the sons of the morn-ing, Dawn on our
dark-ness, and lend us thine aid; Star of the East, the ho-
ri - zon a - dorn-ing, Guide where our in-fant Re-deem-er is laid.

2

Cold on His cradle the dewdrops are
    shining;
    Low lies His head with the beasts
      of the stall.
Angels adore Him in slumber
    reclining,
    Maker and Monarch and Savior of
      all.

3

Shall we not yield Him, in costly
    devotion,
    Odors of Edom and off'rings divine,
Gems of the mountain and pearls
    of the ocean,
    Myrrh from the forest and gold
     from the mine?

4

Vainly we offer each ample oblation,
    Vainly with gifts would His favor
      secure.
Richer by far is the heart's adoration;
    Dearer to God are the prayers of
      the poor.

5

Brightest and best of the sons of the
    morning,
    Dawn on our darkness, and lend us
      thine aid;
Star of the East, the horizon adorn-
    ing,
    Guide where our infant Redeemer
      is laid.

Glory Be to Jesus

Wem in Leidenstagen—6. 5. 6. 5.

Italian, 18th century, cento
Tr., Edward Caswall, 1857

Friedrich Filitz, 1847

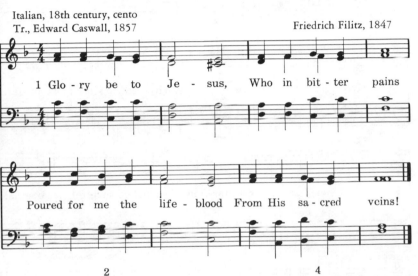

1 Glo - ry be to Je - sus, Who in bit - ter pains
Poured for me the life - blood From His sa - cred veins!

2

Grace and life eternal
    In that blood I find;
Blest be His compassion,
    Infinitely kind!

3

Blest through endless ages
    Be the precious stream
Which from endless torments
    Did the world redeem!

4

Abel's blood for vengeance
    Pleaded to the skies;
But the blood of Jesus
    For our pardon cries.

5

Oft as earth exulting
    Wafts its praise on high,
Angel hosts rejoicing
    Make their glad reply.

6

Lift we, then, our voices,
    Swell the mighty flood,
Louder still and louder
    Praise the precious blood!

Lamb of God, Pure and Holy

O Lamm Gottes, unschuldig—7. 7. 7. 7. 7. 7. 5. 6.

Nikolaus Decius, 1531
Tr., composite

"Christl. Kirchenordnung"
Erfurt, 1542

1 Lamb of God, pure and ho - ly, Who on the cross didst suf-fer,

Ev-er pa-tient and low - ly, Thy-self to scorn didst of-fer.

All sins Thou bor-est for us, Else had de-spair reigned o'er us:

Have mer-cy on us, O— Je - sus! O— Je - sus!

2
Lamb of God, pure and holy,
  Who on the cross didst suffer,
Ever patient and lowly,
  Thyself to scorn didst offer.
All sins Thou borest for us,
Else had despair reigned o'er us:
  Have mercy on us,
    O Jesus! O Jesus!

3
Lamb of God, pure and holy,
  Who on the cross didst suffer,
Ever patient and lowly,
  Thyself to scorn didst offer.
All sins Thou borest for us,
Else had despair reigned o'er us:
  Thy peace be with us,
    O Jesus! O Jesus!

Go to Dark Gethsemane

Gethsemane—7. 7. 7. 7. 7. 7.

James Montgomery, 1820, 1825

Richard Redhead, 1853

1 Go to dark Geth-sem-a-ne, Ye that feel the Tempt-er's pow'r;
Your Re-deem-er's con-flict see, Watch with Him one bit-ter hour;
Turn not from His griefs a-way, Learn of Je-sus Christ to pray.

2
Follow to the judgment hall,
    View the Lord of life arraigned;
Oh, the wormwood and the gall!
    Oh, the pangs His soul sustained!
Shun not suff'ring, shame, or loss;
Learn of Him to bear the cross.

3
Calvary's mournful mountain climb;
    There, adoring at His feet,
Mark that miracle of time,
    God's own sacrifice complete.
"It is finished!" hear Him cry;
Learn of Jesus Christ to die.

4
Early hasten to the tomb
    Where they laid His breathless
        clay;
All is solitude and gloom—
    Who hath taken Him away?
Christ is risen! He meets our eyes.
Savior, teach us so to rise.

Alas! and Did My Savior Bleed

Martyrdom—C. M.

Isaac Watts, 1707, ab.   Hugh Wilson, †1824

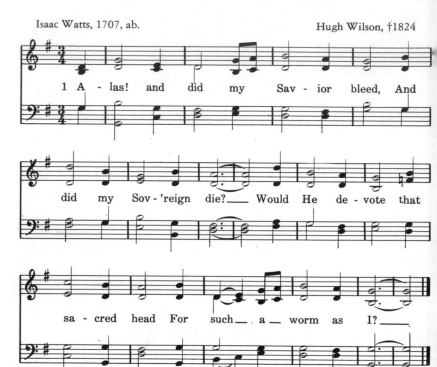

1 A - las! and did my Sav - ior bleed, And did my Sov - 'reign die?__ Would He de - vote that sa - cred head For such __ a __ worm as I?__

2

Was it for crimes that I had done
   He groaned upon the tree?
Amazing pity, grace unknown,
   And love beyond degree!

3

Well might the sun in darkness hide
   And shut His glories in
When God, the mighty Maker, died
   For man the creature's sin.

4

Thus might I hide my blushing face
   While His dear Cross appears,
Dissolve my heart in thankfulness,
   And melt mine eyes to tears.

5

But drops of grief can ne'er repay
   The debt of love I owe;
Here, Lord, I give myself away,
   'Tis all that I can do.

Sweet the Moments, Rich in Blessing

Ringe recht—8. 7. 8. 7.

"Musikalischer Christenschatz"
Basel, 1745

Walter Shirley, 1770, ad., alt.

1 Sweet the mo-ments, rich in bless-ing, Which before the Cross we spend, Life and health and peace pos-
sess-ing From the sin-ners' dy-ing Friend.

2
Here we rest in wonder, viewing
All our sins on Jesus laid;
Here we see redemption flowing
From the sacrifice He made.

3
Here we find the dawn of heaven
While upon the Cross we gaze,
See our trespasses forgiven,
And our songs of triumph raise.

4
Oh, that, near the Cross abiding,
We may to the Savior cleave,
Naught with Him our hearts dividing,
All for Him content to leave!

5
Lord, in loving contemplation
Fix our hearts and eyes on Thee
Till we taste Thy full salvation
And Thine unveiled glory see.

O Lamb of God Most Lowly

Christus, der ist mein—7. 6. 7. 6.

Author unknown

Melchior Vulpius, 1609

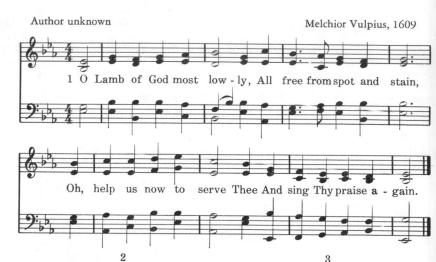

1 O Lamb of God most low-ly, All free from spot and stain,

Oh, help us now to serve Thee And sing Thy praise a-gain.

2

O Lamb of God most holy,
　So great, and yet so meek,
May we, when pride allures us,
　Thy lowly spirit seek.

3

O Lamb of God most gentle,
　So kind and good and true,
May we, when passion tempts us,
　Thy gentleness pursue.

4

O Lamb of God most lovely;
　To Thee our faith would flee;
Reveal to us Thy beauty,
　And win our hearts to Thee.

38

O Christ, Thou Lamb of God

Christe, du Lamm Gottes—Irregular

From the German, 1528
Tr., unknown

Johann Bugenhagen's "Kirchenordnung"
Braunschweig, 1528

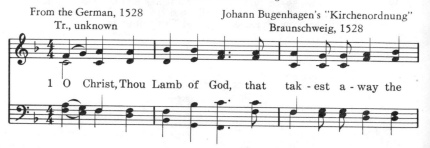

1 O Christ, Thou Lamb of God, that tak-est a-way the

sin of the world, have mer - cy up - on us!

O Christ, Thou Lamb of God, that tak - est a -way the

sin of the world, have mer - cy up - on us!

O Christ, Thou Lamb of God, that tak - est a -way the

sin of the world, grant us Thy peace! __ A - - men.

Christ, the Life of All the Living

Jesu, meines Lebens Leben—8. 7. 8. 7. 8. 8. 7. 7.

Ernst C. Homburg, 1659, ab.
Tr., Catherine Winkworth, 1863, alt., cento

"Kirchengesangbuch"
Darmstadt, 1687

1 Christ, the Life of all the liv-ing, Christ, the Death of death, our foe, Who, Thy-self for me once giv-ing To the dark-est depths of woe Through Thy suf-f'rings, death, and mer-it I e-ter-nal life in-her-it. Thou-sand, thou-sand thanks shall be, Dear-est Je-sus, un-to Thee.

2

Thou hast suffered great affliction
  And hast borne it patiently,
Even death by crucifixion,
  Fully to atone for me;
Thou didst choose to be tormented
That my doom should be prevented.
    Thousand, thousand thanks shall
      be,
    Dearest Jesus, unto Thee.

3

Then, for all that wrought my
      pardon,
  For Thy sorrows deep and sore,
For Thine anguish in the Garden,
  I will thank Thee evermore,
Thank Thee for Thy groaning,
      sighing,
For Thy bleeding and Thy dying
  For that last triumphant cry,
  And shall praise Thee, Lord, on
    high.

40

Jesus, All Our Ransom Paid

Septem Verba—7. 7. 7. 6.

Thomas B. Pollock, 1870   Bernhard Schumacher, 1939

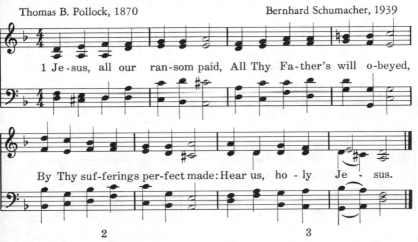

1 Je-sus, all our ran-som paid, All Thy Fa-ther's will o-beyed,

By Thy suf-ferings per-fect made: Hear us, ho-ly Je - sus.

2

Save us in our soul's distress,
Be our Help to cheer and bless
While we grow in holiness:
  Hear us, holy Jesus.

3

Brighten all our heavenward way
With an ever holier ray
Till we pass to perfect day:
  Hear us, holy Jesus.

4

May Thy life and death supply
Grace to live and grace to die,
Grace to reach the home on high:
  Hear us, holy Jesus.

O Sacred Head, Now Wounded

Herzlich tut mich—7. 6. 7. 6. D.

Based on the Latin
Bernard of Clairvaux, †1153, asc.
Paul Gerhardt, 1656, cento   Tr., composite

Hans L. Hassler, 1601

1 O sa-cred Head, now wound-ed, With grief and shame weighed down,
Now scorn-ful-ly sur-round-ed With thorns, Thine on-ly crown.
O sa-cred Head, what glo - ry, What bliss, till now was Thine!
Yet, though de-spised and go - ry, I joy to call Thee mine.

2

My burden in Thy Passion,
  Lord, Thou hast borne for me,
For it was my transgression
  Which bro't this woe on Thee.
I cast me down before thee;
  Wrath were my rightful lot.
Have mercy, I implore Thee;
  Redeemer, spurn me not!

3

My Shepherd, now receive me;
  My Guardian, own me Thine.
Great blessings Thou didst give me,
  O Source of gifts divine.
Thy lips have often fed me
  With words of truth and love;
Thy Spirit oft hath led me
  To heavenly joys above.

4

Be Thou my Consolation,
  My Shield, when I must die;
Remind me of Thy Passion
  When my last hour draws nigh.
Mine eyes shall then behold Thee,
  Upon Thy Cross shall dwell,
My heart by faith enfold Thee.
  Who dieth thus dies well.

42

When I Survey the Wondrous Cross

Hamburg—L. M.

Issac Watts, 1707, ab. and alt.

Based on First Gregorian Chant
Arr. by Lowell Mason, 1824

1 When I sur-vey the won-drous Cross On which the Prince of Glo-ry died,

My rich-est gain I count but loss And pour con-tempt on all my pride.

2

Forbid it, Lord, that I should boast
  Save in the death of Christ, my
    God;
All the vain things that charm me
    most,
  I sacrifice them to His blood.

3

See, from His head, His hands,
    His feet,
  Sorrow and love flow mingled
    down.
Did e'er such love and sorrow meet
  Or thorns compose so rich a crown?

4

Were the whole realm of nature mine,
  That were a tribute far too small;
Love so amazing, so divine,
  Demands my soul, my life, my all.

There Is a Green Hill Far Away

Horsley—C. M.

Cecil Frances Alexander, 1848   William Horsley, 1844

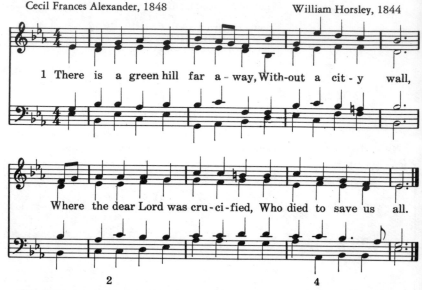

1 There is a green hill far a-way, With-out a cit-y wall,

Where the dear Lord was cru-ci-fied, Who died to save us all.

2

We may not know, we cannot tell,
    What pains He had to bear,
But we believe it was for us
    He hung and suffered there.

3

He died that we might be forgiven,
    He died to make us good,
That we might go at last to heaven,
    Saved by His precious blood.

4

There was no other good enough
    To pay the price of sin,
He only could unlock the gate
    Of heaven and let us in.

5

Oh, dearly, dearly has He loved!
    And we must love Him too
And trust in His redeeming blood,
    And try His works to do.

See also:
    My Faith Looks Up to Thee
    Jesus, Thy Blood and Righteousness
    My Hope Is Built on Nothing Less
    There Is a Fountain Filled with Blood
    We Sing the Praise of Him Who Died
    Drawn to the Cross, Which Thou Hast Blest
    In the Cross of Christ I Glory

Christ the Lord Is Risen Today

Orientis partibus—7. 7. 7. 7.

Charles Wesley, 1739, cento

French melody, c. 1200, ad.

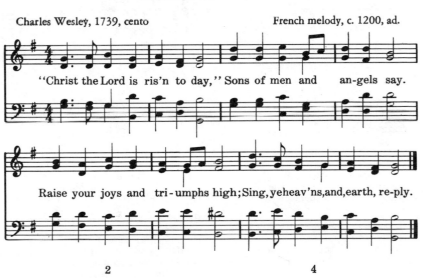

"Christ the Lord is ris'n to day," Sons of men and an-gels say.

Raise your joys and tri-umphs high; Sing, ye heav'ns, and, earth, re-ply.

2

Love's redeeming work is done,
Fought the fight, the battle won.
Lo, our Sun's eclipse is o'er;
Lo, He sets in blood no more.

3

Vain the stone, the watch, the seal;
Christ has burst the gates of hell.
Death in vain forbids His rise;
Christ has opened Paradise.

4

Lives again our glorious King;
Where, O Death, is now thy sting?
Once He died our souls to save;
Where thy victory, O Grave?

5

Soar we now where Christ has led,
Following our exalted Head.
Made like Him, like Him we rise;
Ours the cross, the grave, the skies.

I Know that My Redeemer Lives

Duke Street—L. M.

Samuel Medley, 1775, ab.

John Hatton, 1793

1 I know that my Re - deem - er lives;What com -fort this sweet sen-tence gives! He lives, He lives, who once was dead; He lives, my ev - er - liv - ing Head.

2
He lives triumphant from the grave,
He lives eternally to save,
He lives all-glorious in the sky,
He lives exalted there on high.

3
He lives to bless me with His love,
He lives to plead for me above,
He lives my hungry soul to feed,
He lives to help in time of need.

4
He lives to grant me rich supply,
He lives to guide me with His eye,
He lives to comfort me when faint,
He lives to hear my soul's complaint.

5
He lives to silence all my fears,
He lives to wipe away my tears,
He lives to calm my troubled heart,
He lives all blessings to impart.

6
He lives, my kind, wise, heavenly
    Friend,
He lives and loves me to the end;
He lives, and while He lives, I'll sing;
He lives, my Prophet, Priest, and
    King.

7
He lives and grants me daily breath;
He lives, and I shall conquer death;
He lives my mansion to prepare;
He lives to bring me safely there.

8
He lives, all glory to His name!
He lives, my Jesus, still the same.
Oh, the sweet joy this sentence gives,
"I know that my Redeemer lives!"

Awake, My Heart, with Gladness

Auf, auf, mein Herz—7. 6. 7. 6. 6. 6. 6. 6.

Paul Gerhardt, 1648, ab.
Tr., John Kelly, 1867, alt.

Johann Crueger, 1648

1 A-wake, my heart, with glad - ness, See what to-day is done;

Now, af-ter gloom and sad - ness, Comes forth the glo-rious Sun.

My Sav-ior there was laid Where our bed must be made

When to the realms of light Our spir-it wings its flight.

2

The Foe in triumph shouted
  When Christ lay in the tomb;
But, lo, he now is routed,
  His boast is turned to gloom.
For Christ again is free;
  In glorious victory
He who is strong to save
  Has triumphed o'er the grave.

3

This is a sight that gladdens;
  What peace it doth impart!
Now nothing ever saddens
  The joy within my heart.
No gloom shall ever shake,
  No foe shall ever take,
The hope which God's own Son
  In love for me hath won.

Ye Sons and Daughters of the King

Gelobt sei Gott— 8. 8. 8, with Alleluias

Author unknown, c. 1600
Tr., John M. Neale, 1851, ab.

Melchior Vulpius, 1609

1 Ye sons and daugh-ters of the King, Whom heav'n-ly hosts in glo - ry sing, To-day the grave hath lost its sting.

Al - le - lu - ia! Al - le - lu - ia! Al - le - lu - ia!

2
On that first morning of the week,
Before the day began to break,
The Marys went their Lord to seek.
Alleluia!

3
An angel bade their sorrow flee,
For thus he spake unto the three:
"Your Lord is gone to Galilee."
Alleluia!

4
That night th' Apostles met in fear,
Amidst them came their Lord most
dear
And said: "Peace be unto you here."
Alleluia!

5
When Thomas afterwards had heard
That Jesus had fulfilled His word,
He doubted if it were the Lord.
Alleluia!

6

"Thomas, behold My side," saith He,
"My hands, My feet, My body, see;
And doubt not, but believe in Me."
    Alleluia!

7

No longer Thomas then denied;
He saw the feet, the hands, the side;
"Thou art my Lord and God," he
    cried.
        Alleluia!

8

Blessed are they that have not seen
And yet whose faith hath constant
    been,
In life eternal they shall reign.
    Alleluia!

48

Easter Flowers Are Blooming Bright

Keine Schoenheit hat die Welt—7. 7. 7. 7.

Mary A. Nicholson, 1875   Scheffler's "Seelenlust," 1657

1 East - er flow'rs are bloom-ing bright, East-er skies pour ra-diant light,
Christ, our Lord, is ris'n in might: Glo - ry in the high - est.

2

Angels caroled this sweet lay,
When in manger rude He lay.
Now, once more cast grief away:
    Glory in the highest!

3

He, then, born to grief and pain
Now to glory born again,
Calleth forth our gladdest strain:
    Glory in the highest!

4

As He riseth, rise we too,
Tune we heart and voice anew,
Off'ring praises glad and true:
    Glory in the highest!

He Is Risen! He Is Risen!

Neander—8. 7. 8. 7. 7. 7.

Cecil Frances Alexander, 1846, alt.   Joachim Neander, 1680

1 He is ris-en! He is ris-en! Tell it with a joy-ful voice;

He has burst His three days' pris-on; Let the whole wide earth re-joice:

Death is con-quered, man is free, Christ has won the vic-to-ry.

2

Tell it to the sinners, weeping
  Over deeds in darknss done,
Weary watch of sorrow keeping,
  Brightly breaks their Easter sun;
Blood can wash all sins away,
Christ has conquered hell today.

3

Come, with high and holy gladness,
  Chant our Lord's triumphant lay;
Not one touch of twilight sadness
  Dims His resurrection day;
Brightly dawns the radiant East,
Brighter far our Easter Feast.

4

He is risen! He is risen!
  He has opened heaven's gate;
We are free from sin's dark prison,
  Risen to a holier state;
Soon a brighter Easter beam
On our longing eyes shall stream.

The Eastertide with Joy Was Bright

Lasst uns erfreuen—L. M., with Alleluias

Tr., John M. Neale, 1818-1866

"Geistliche Kirchengesaeng"
Cologne, 1623

1 The East-er-tide with joy was bright, The sun shone out with fair-er light,
Al - le - lu - ia! Al-le-lu - ia! When, to their long-ing eyes re-stored,
Th' A - pos-tles saw their ris - en Lord. Al-le - lu - ia! Al-le -
lu - ia! Al-le - lu - ia! Al-le - lu - ia! Al-le - lu - ia!

2
He bade them see His hands, His side,
Where yet the glorious wounds abide,
    Alleluia!
The tokens true which made it plain
Their Lord, indeed, was ris'n again.
    Alleluia!

3
O Lord of all, with us abide
In this our joyful Eastertide.
    Alleluia!
From every weapon death can wield
Thine own redeemed forever shield.
    Alleluia!

Jesus Christ Is Risen Today, Alleluia!

Easter Hymn—7. 7. 7. 7, with Alleluias

Author unknown, c. 1372
Tr. unknown, 1708-1882

"Lyra Davidica," 1708, alt.

1 Je - sus Christ is ris'n to - day, Al - le - lu - ia!

Our tri - um-phant ho - ly day, Al - le - lu - ia!

Who did once up - on the cross, Al - le - lu - ia!

Suf-fer to re - deem our loss. Al - le - lu - ia!

2

Hymns of praise, then, let us sing.
　　Alleluia!
Unto Christ, our heav'nly King,
　　Alleluia!
Who endured the cross and grave,
　　Alleluia!
Sinners to redeem and save.
　　Alleluia!

3

But the pains which He endured,
　　Alleluia!
Our salvation have procured.
　　Alleluia!
Now above the sky He's King,
　　Alleluia!
Where the angels ever sing.
　　Alleluia!

4

Sing we to our God above,
　　Alleluia!
Praise eternal as His love:
　　Alleluia!
Praise Him. all ye heav'nly host,
　　Alleluia!
Father. Son, and Holy Ghost.
　　Alleluia!

On Wings of Living Light

Darwall's 148th—6. 6. 6. 6. 8. 8.

William W. How, 1872

John Darwall, 1770

1 On wings of liv-ing light, At ear-liest dawn of day, Came down the an-gel bright And rolled the stone a-way. Your voic-es raise with one ac-cord To bless and praise your ris-en Lord.

2
The keepers watching near,
   At that dread sight and sound,
Fell down with sudden fear,
   Like dead men, to the ground.
Your voices raise with one accord
To bless and praise your risen Lord.

3
Then rose from death's dark gloom,
   Unseen by human eye,
Triumphant o'er the tomb,
   The Lord of earth and sky.
Your voices raise with one accord
To bless and praise your risen Lord.

4
Leave in the grave beneath
   The old things passed away;
Buried with Him in death,
   Oh, live with Him today.
Your voices raise with one accord
To bless and praise your risen Lord.

Angels, Roll the Rock Away

Hendon—7. 7. 7. 7.

Thomas Scott, 1769

H. A. Cesar Malan, 1827

1 An-gels, roll the rock a-way; Death, yield up thy might-y prey; See, the Sav-ior leaves the tomb, Glow-ing with im-mor-tal bloom, Glow-ing with im-mor-tal bloom.

2
Saints on earth, lift up your eyes;
Now to glory see Him rise
In long triumph through the sky
Up to waiting worlds on high.

3
Heav'n unfolds its portals wide;
Mighty Conqu'ror, through them ride.
King of Glory, mount Thy throne,
Boundless empire is Thine own.

4
Pow'rs of heaven, angel choirs,
Sing and play your golden lyres;
Sons of men, in humbler strain,
Sing your mighty Savior's reign.

See also:
We Welcome Glad Easter
We Will Carol Joyfully
Come, Ye Children, Sing to Jesus

54

Jesus, King of Glory

Sei du mir gegruesset—6. 5. 6. 5. D., with Refrain

W. Hope Davison, 1827-1894

"Enchiridion"
Luebeck, 1545

1 Je-sus, King of Glo-ry, Throned a-bove the sky,

Je-sus, ten-der Sav-ior, Hear Thy chil-dren cry.

Par-don our trans-gres-sions, Cleanse us from our sin;

By Thy Spir-it help us Heav'n-ly life to win.

Je - sus, King of Glo - ry, Throned a - bove the sky,

Je - sus, ten - der Sav - ior, Hear Thy chil - dren cry.

2

On this day of gladness,
　Bending low the knee
In Thine earthly temple,
　Lord, we worship Thee;
Celebrate Thy goodness,
　Mercy, grace, and truth,
All the loving guidance
　Of our heedless youth.
Jesus, King of Glory,
　Throned above the sky,
Jesus, tender Savior,
　Hear Thy children cry.

3

For the little children
　Who have come to Thee;
For the holy angels
　Who Thy glory see;
For the loved ones resting
　In Thy dear embrace;
For the pure and holy
　Who behold Thy face.
Jesus, King of Glory,
　Throned above the sky,
Jesus, tender Savior,
　Hear Thy children cry.

4

Help us ever steadfast
　In the faith to be,
In Thy Church's conflicts
　Fighting valiantly.
Loving Savior, strengthen
　These weak hearts of ours,
Through Thy Cross to conquer
　Crafty evil powers.
Jesus, King of Glory,
　Throned above the sky,
Jesus, tender Savior,
　Hear Thy children cry.

A Hymn of Glory Let Us Sing

Lasst uns erfreuen—L. M., with Alleluias

The Venerable Bede, †735, cento
Tr., Benjamin Webb, 1854, alt.

"Geistliche Kirchengesaeng"
Cologne, 1623

1 A hymn of glo-ry let us sing; New songs thro'out the world shall ring: Al-le - lu - ia! Al-le - lu - ia! Christ, by a road be-fore un - trod, As - cend-eth to the throne of God. Al-le - lu - ia! Al-le - lu - ia!

Al-le - lu - ia! Al-le - lu - ia! Al-le - lu - ia!

2
The holy apostolic band
Upon the Mount of Olives stand;
    Alleluia! Alleluia!
And with His followers they see
Jesus' resplendent majesty.
    Alleluia! Alleluia! Alleluia!

3
O risen Christ, ascended Lord,
All praise to Thee let earth accord,
    Alleluia! Alleluia!
Who art, while endless ages run,
With Father and with Spirit One.
    Alleluia! Alleluia! Alleluia!

56

Hail the Day That Sees Him Rise

Orientis partibus—7. 7. 7. 7.

Charles Wesley, 1739, cento, alt.   French melody, c. 1200, ad.

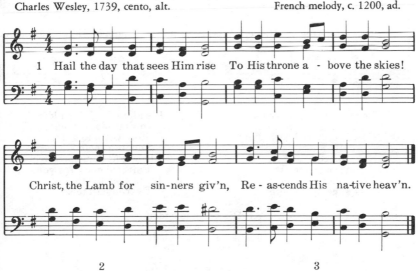

1 Hail the day that sees Him rise To His throne a - bove the skies!

Christ, the Lamb for sin-ners giv'n, Re - as-cends His na-tive heav'n.

2
See, He lifts His hands above;
See, He shows the prints of love.
Hark! His gracious lips bestow
Blessings on His Church below.

3
Still for us He intercedes;
His atoning death He pleads,
Near Himself prepares a place,
For the sinners saved by grace.

Golden Harps Are Sounding

Gute Baeume bringen—6. 5. 6. 5. D.

Frances R. Havergal, 1871   P. Sohren, d.c. 1692

1 Gold-en harps are sound-ing, An-gel voic-es sing, Heaven's gates are o-pened, O-pened for the King, Je-sus, King of Glo-ry, Je-sus, King of Love, Is gone up in tri-umph To His throne a-bove.

2
He who came to save us,
  He who bled and died,
Now is crowned with glory
  At His Father's side,
Nevermore to suffer,
  Nevermore to die.
Jesus, King of Glory,
  Is gone up on high.

3
Pleading for His children
  In that blessed place,
Calling them to glory,
  Sending them His grace,
His bright home preparing,
  Faithful ones, for you,
Jesus ever liveth,
  Ever loveth too.

4
All His work is ended,
  Joyfully we sing,
Jesus hath ascended!
  Glory to our King!
Jesus, King of Glory,
  Jesus, King of Love,
Is gone up in triumph
  To His throne above.

Draw Us to Thee

Ach Gott und Herr—4. 4. 7. 4. 4. 7.

Friedrich Funcke, 1686
Tr., August Crull, †1923

C. Peter, "Andachts-Zymbeln"
Freyberg, 1655

1 Draw us to Thee, For then shall we Walk in Thy steps for - ev - er And hast - en on Where Thou art gone To be with Thee, dear Sav - ior.

2
Draw us to Thee, Lord, lovingly;
  Let us depart with gladness
That we may be forever free
  From sorrow, grief, and sadness.

3
Draw us to Thee; oh, grant that we
  May walk the road to heaven!
Direct our way lest we should stray
  And from Thy paths be driven.

4
Draw us to Thee that also we
  Thy heavenly bliss inherit
And ever dwell where sin and hell
  No more can vex our spirit.

5
Draw us to Thee unceasingly,
  Into Thy kingdom take us;
Let us fore'er Thy glory share,
  Thy saints and joint heirs make us.

See also:
  All Hail the Power of Jesus' Name
  Crown Him with Many Crowns

59

Holy Ghost, with Light Divine

Light Divine—7. 7. 7. 7.

Andrew Reed, 1817, cento

Orlando Gibbons, 1623

1 Ho-ly Ghost, with light di-vine Shine up-on this heart of mine;

Chase the shades of night a-way, Turn the dark-ness in-to day.

2
Let me see my Savior's face,
Let me all His beauties trace;
Show those glorious truths to me
Which are only known to Thee.

3
Holy Ghost, with pow'r divine
Cleanse this guilty heart of mine;
In Thy mercy pity me,
From sin's bondage set me free.

4
Holy Ghost, with joy divine
Cheer this saddened heart of mine;
Yield a sacred, settled peace,
Let it grow and still increase.

5
Holy Spirit, all divine,
Dwell within this heart of mine;
Cast down every idol throne,
Reign supreme, and reign alone.

6
See, to Thee I yield my heart,
Shed Thy life through every part;
A pure temple I would be,
Wholly dedicate to Thee.

Holy Spirit, Hear Us

Wem in Leidenstagen—6. 5. 6. 5.

From the German by
Joseph Mohr, 1816
Tr., Claudia F. Hernaman, 1838-1898

Friedrich Filitz, 1847

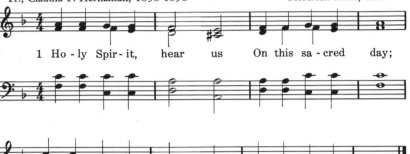

1 Ho - ly Spir - it, hear us On this sa - cred day;

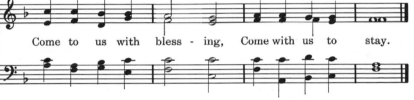

Come to us with bless - ing, Come with us to stay.

2

Come as once Thou camest
   To the faithful few
Patiently awaiting
   Jesus' promise true.

3

Up to heav'n ascending,
   Our dear Lord has gone;
Yet His little children
   Leaves He not alone.

4

To His blessed promise
   Now in faith we cling.
Comforter, most holy,
   Spread o'er us Thy wing.

5

Lighten Thou our darkness,
   Be Thyself our Light;
Strengthen Thou our weakness,
   Spirit of all might.

6

Spirit of Adoption,
   Make us overflow
With Thy sevenfold blessing
   And in grace to grow.

7

Into Christ baptized,
   Grant that we may be
Day and night, dear Spirit,
   Perfected by Thee.

61

O Holy Spirit, Enter In

Wie schoen leuchtet—8. 8. 7. 8. 8. 7. 4. 4. 4. 4. 8.

Michael Schirmer, 1640, alt.
Tr., Catherine Winkworth, 1863, alt.

Philipp Nicolai, 1599

1 O Ho - ly Spir - it, en - ter in, And in our hearts Thy work be - gin, Thy tem - ple deign to make us; Sun of the soul, Thou Light Di - vine, A - round and

in us bright-ly shine, To joy and glad-ness wake us

That we, In Thee Tru - ly liv - ing, To Thee giv - ing

Prayer un-ceas-ing, May in love be still in-creas - ing.

2

Give to Thy Word impressive pow'r
That in our hearts, from this good
    hour,
  As fire it may be glowing;
That we confess the Father, Son,
And Thee, the Spirit, Three in One,
  Thy glory ever showing.
Stay Thou, Guide now
Our souls ever That they never
May forsake Thee,
But by faith their Refuge make Thee.

62

Come, Holy Ghost, God and Lord

Komm, Heiliger Geist, Herre Gott--7. 8. 8. 8. 8. 8. 8. 8.10. 8.

Martin Luther, 1524
Tr., composite

15th-century melody

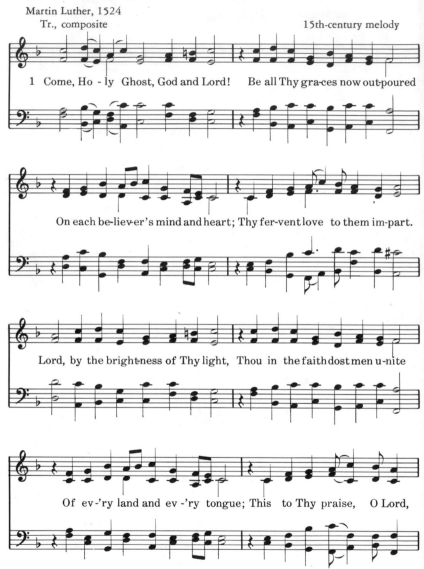

1 Come, Ho - ly Ghost, God and Lord! Be all Thy gra-ces now out-poured

On each be-liev-er's mind and heart; Thy fer-vent love to them im-part.

Lord, by the bright-ness of Thy light, Thou in the faith dost men u-nite

Of ev-'ry land and ev-'ry tongue; This to Thy praise, O Lord,

our God, be sung. Hal - le - lu - jah! Hal - le - lu - jah!

2
Thou holy Light, Guide Divine,
Oh, cause the Word of Life to shine!
Teach us to know our God aright
And call Him Father with delight.
From ev'ry error keep us free;
Let none but Christ our Master be
That we in living faith abide,
In Him, our Lord, with all our might
   confide.
   Hallelujah! Hallelujah!

3
Thou holy Fire, Comfort true,
Grant us the will Thy work to do
And in Thy service to abide;
Let trials turn us not aside.
Lord, by Thy pow'r prepare each
   heart
And to our weakness strength impart
That bravely here we may contend,
Through life and death to Thee, our
   Lord, ascend.
   Hallelujah! Hallelujah!

63

Come, Holy Spirit, Come

Franconia—S. M.

"Harmonischer Liederschatz"
Frankfurt, 1738

Dorothy A. Thrupp, 1779-1847

1. Come, Ho - ly Spir - it, come; Oh, hear my hum - ble prayer!

Stoop down and make my heart Thy home, And shed Thy bless-ing there.

2
Thy light, Thy love impart,
   And let it ever be
A holy, humble, happy heart,
   A dwelling place for Thee.

3
Let Thy rich grace increase
   Through all my early days
The fruits of righteousness and peace
   To Thine eternal praise.

Gracious Spirit, Dove Divine

Culbach—7. 7. 7. 7.

John Stocker, 1777

"Heilige Seelenlust"
Breslau, 1657, ad.

1 Gra-cious Spir-it, Dove Di - vine, Let Thy light with-in me shine,

All. my guilt - y fears re-move, Fill me with Thy heav'n-ly love.

2
Speak Thy pardoning grace to me,
Set the burdened sinner free,
Lead me to the Lamb of God,
Wash me in His precious blood.

3
Life and peace to me impart;
Seal salvation in my heart,
Dwell Thyself within my breast,
And bestow eternal rest.

4
Let me never from Thee stray,
Keep me in the narrow way,
Fill my soul with joy divine,
Keep me, Lord, forever Thine.

We All Believe in One True God

Wir glauben all' an einen Gott—8. 7. 7. 7. 7. 7.

Tobias Clausnitzer, 1668
Tr., Catherine Winkworth, 1863, alt.

"Kirchengesangbuch"
Darmstadt, 1699

1 We all be-lieve in one true God, Fa-ther, Son, and Ho -ly Ghost,

Ev - er-pres-ent Help in need, Praised by all the heav'n - ly host,

By whose might-y pow'r a -lone All is made and wrought and done.

2
We all believe in Jesus Christ,
  Son of God and Mary's Son,
Who descended from His throne
  And for us salvation won;
By whose Cross and death are we
Rescued from all misery.

3
We all confess the Holy Ghost,
  Who from both fore'er proceeds;
Who upholds and comforts us
  In all trials, fears, and needs.
Blest and Holy Trinity,
Praise forever be to Thee!

Holy, Holy, Holy, Lord God Almighty

Nicaea—11. 12. 12. 10.

Reginald Heber, 1827

John B. Dykes, 1861

1. Ho - ly, ho - ly, ho - ly! Lord God Al - might - y!

Ear - ly in the morn - ing our song shall rise to Thee;

Ho - ly, ho - ly, ho - ly, mer - ci - ful and might - y!

God in Three Per - sons, bless-ed Trin - i - ty!

2

Holy, holy, holy! All the saints
  adore Thee,
Casting down their golden crowns
  around the glassy sea;
Cherubim and seraphim falling
  down before Thee,
Which wert and art and evermore
  shalt be.

3

Holy, holy, holy! Though the darkness
  hide Thee,
Though the eye of sinful man Thy
  glory may not see,
Only Thou art holy; there is none
  beside Thee,
Perfect in pow'r, in love, and purity.

4

Holy, holy, holy! Lord God Almighty!
All Thy works shall praise Thy name
  in earth and sky and sea.
Holy, holy, holy, merciful and
  mighty!
God in Three Persons, blessed Trinity!

67

Glory to the Father Give

Culbach—7. 7. 7. 7.

"Heilige Seelenlust"
Breslau, 1657, ad.

James Montgomery, 1771-1854

1 Glo-ry to the Fa-ther give, God in whom we move and live;

Chil-dren's pray'rs He deigns to hear, Chil-dren's songs de-light His ear.

2

Glory to the Son we bring,
Christ, our Prophet, Priest, and King;
Children, raise your sweetest strain
To the Lamb, for He was slain.

3

Glory to the Holy Ghost,
Who reclaims the sinner lost;
Children's minds may He inspire,
Touch their tongues with holy fire.

4

Glory in the highest be
To the blessed Trinity,
For the Gospel from above,
For the Word that God is Love.

68

Come, Thou Almighty King

Italian Hymn—6. 6. 4. 6. 6. 6. 4.

Author unknown, c. 1757, ab.   Felice de Giardini, 1769

1 Come, Thou al - might y King, Help us Thy name to sing,
Help us to praise. Fa - ther all - glo - ri - ous, O'er all vic -
to - ri - ous, Come and reign o - ver us, An - cient of Days.

2
Come, Thou Incarnate Word,
Gird on Thy mighty sword,
    Our prayer attend.
Come and Thy people bless,
And give Thy Word success;
Stablish Thy righteousness,
    Savior and Friend!

3
Come, holy Comforter,
Thy sacred witness bear
    In this glad hour.
Thou, who almighty art,
Now rule in ev'ry heart,
And ne'er from us depart,
    Spirit of Pow'r!

4
To the great One in Three
Eternal praises be
    Hence evermore!
His sov'reign majesty
May we in glory see
And to eternity
    Love and adore!

Holy, Holy, Holy, Lord

Fred til Bod—7. 7. 7. 7. 7. 7.

Christopher Wordsworth, 1862, cento

Ludvig M. Lindeman, 1871

1 Ho-ly, ho-ly, ho-ly, Lord God of Hosts, e-ter-nal King,

By the heav'ns and earth a-dored; An-gels and arch-an-gels sing,

Chant-ing ev-er-last-ing-ly To the bless-ed Trin-i-ty.

2

Since by Thee were all things made
And in Thee do all things live,
Be to Thee all honor paid,
Praise to Thee let all things give,
Singing everlastingly
To the blessed Trinity.

3

Alleluia! Lord, to Thee,
Father, Son, and Holy Ghost,
Three in One, and One in Three,
Join we with the heavenly host,
Singing everlastingly
To the blessed Trinity.

Glory Be to God the Father

Worcester—8. 7. 8. 7. 4. 7.

Horatius Bonar, 1866

Walter G. Whinfield, †1919

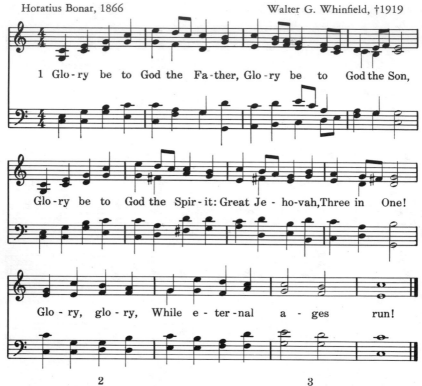

1 Glo-ry be to God the Fa-ther, Glo-ry be to God the Son,

Glo-ry be to God the Spir-it: Great Je-ho-vah, Three in One!

Glo-ry, glo-ry, While e-ter-nal a-ges run!

2
Glory be to Him who loved us,
　Washed us from each spot and
　　stain;
Glory be to Him who bought us,
　Made us kings with Him to reign!
　　Glory, glory,
　To the Lamb that once was slain!

3
Glory to the King of angels,
　Glory to the Church's King,
Glory to the King of nations;
　Heav'n and earth, your praises
　　bring!
　　Glory, glory,
　To the King of Glory sing!

4
Glory, blessing, praise eternal!
　Thus the choir of angels sings;
Honor, riches, pow'r, dominion!
　Thus its praise creation brings.
　　Glory, glory,
　Glory to the King of Kings!

Blessed Father, Great Creator

Regent Square—8. 7. 8. 7. 8. 7.

John Cawood, 1837

Henry Smart, 1867

1 Bless-ed Fa-ther, great Cre-a-tor, Hum-bly at Thy feet we bend;

To Thy throne for all Thy fa-vor Youth-ful prais-es now we send.

Bless-ed Fa-ther, bless-ed Fa-ther, To our youth-ful songs at-tend.

2
Blessed Jesus, great Redeemer,
Sadly by Thy cross we stand;
On that cross Thou diedst to bring us
To the joys of Thy right hand.
Blessed Jesus, blessed Jesus,
Bring us to Thy heavenly land.

3
Blessed Spirit, great Consoler,
Make our hearts Thy dwelling
place;
Teach us, guide us, sanctify us,
And console us all our days.
Blessed Spirit, blessed Spirit,
Ever cheer us with Thy grace.

4
Blessed Father, Son, and Spirit,
Glorious Godhead, Three in One,
Guide us to the heaven of heavens,
Through the merits of the Son.
Guide and guard us, guide and
guard us,
Till we see Him on the throne.

72

A Mighty Fortress Is Our God

Ein' feste Burg—8. 7. 8. 7. 5. 5. 5. 6. 7.

Martin Luther, 1529
Tr., composite

Martin Luther, 1529

1 A might-y For-tress is our God, A trust-y Shield and Weap - on;

He helps us free from ev - 'ry need That hath us now o'er-tak - en.

The old e - vil Foe Now means dead-ly woe;

Deep guile and great might   Are his dread arms   in   fight;

On earth   is   not   his   e   -   qual.

2

With might of ours can naught be
    done,
    Soon were our loss effected;
But for us fights the Valiant One,
    Whom God Himself elected.
Ask ye, Who is this?
Jesus Christ it is,
Of Sabaoth Lord,
And there's none other God;
    He holds the field forever.

3

Though devils all the world should fill,
    All eager to devour us,
We tremble not, we fear no ill,
    They shall not overpow'r us.
This world's prince may still
Scowl fierce as he will,
He can harm us none,
He's judged; the deed is done;
    One little word can fell him.

4

The Word they still shall let remain
    Nor any thanks have for it;
He's by our side upon the plain
    With His good gifts and Spirit.
And take they our life,
Goods, fame, child, and wife,
Let these all be gone,
They yet have nothing won;
    The Kingdom ours remaineth.

73

Built on the Rock the Church Doth Stand

Kirken den er et—8. 8. 8. 8. 8. 8. 8. 8.

Nicolai F. S. Grundtvig, 1837
Tr., Carl Doeving, 1909, alt.

Ludvig M. Lindeman, 1871

1 Built on the Rock the Church doth stand, E-ven when stee-ples are fall - ing; Crum-bled have spires in ev - 'ry land, Bells still are chim-ing and call - ing, Call-ing the young and old to rest, But a-bove all the soul dis - trest, Long-ing for rest ev - er - last - ing.

2

Surely in temples made with hands,
  God, the Most High, is not
    dwelling;
High above earth His temple stands,
  All earthly temples excelling.
Yet He whom heav'ns cannot contain
Chose to abide on earth with men,
  Built in our bodies His temple.

3

We are God's house of living stones,
  Builded for His habitation;
He through baptismal grace us owns
  Heirs of His wondrous salvation.
Were we but two His name to tell,
Yet He would deign with us to dwell,
  With all His grace and His favor.

74

Lord, Keep Us Steadfast in Thy Word

Erhalt uns, Herr—L. M.

Martin Luther, 1541
Tr., Catherine Winkworth, 1863

"Geistliche Lieder"
Wittenberg, 1543

1 Lord, keep us stead-fast in Thy Word; Curb those who

fain by craft and sword Would wrest the King-dom from Thy

Son And set at naught all He hath done.

2

Lord Jesus Christ, Thy pow'r make
    known,
For Thou art Lord of Lords alone;
Defend Thy Christendom that we
May evermore sing praise to Thee.

3

O Comforter of priceless worth,
Send peace and unity on earth.
Support us in our final strife,
And lead us out of death to life.

75

Lord, Open Thou My Heart to Hear

Erhalt uns, Herr—L. M.

Johannes Olearius, 1671
Tr., Matthias Loy, 1880

"Geistliche Lieder"
Wittenberg, 1543

1 Lord, o-pen Thou my heart to hear And through Thy Word to me draw near; Let me Thy Word e'er pure re-tain, Let me Thy child and heir re-main.

2
Thy Word doth deeply move the heart,
Thy Word doth perfect health impart,
Thy Word my soul with joy doth bless,
Thy Word brings peace and happiness.

3
To God the Father, God the Son,
And God the Spirit, Three in One,
Shall glory, praise, and honor be
Now and throughout eternity.

O Dearest Lord, by All Adored

Nun freut euch—8. 7. 8. 7. 8. 8. 7.

Maurice F. Bell, 1862-1931

"Etlich' christliche Lieder"
Wittenberg, 1524

O dear-est Lord, by all a-dored, Our tres-pass-es con - fess - ing,

To Thee this day Thy chil-dren pray, The ho-ly faith pro - fess - ing.

Ac - cept, O King, the gifts we bring, Our songs of praise, the

prayers we raise, **And** grant us, Lord, Thy bless - ing.

Words from *The English Hymnal.* Copyright, Oxford University Press.
Used by permission.

77

Blessed Jesus, at Thy Word

Liebster Jesu—7. 8. 7. 8. 8. 8.

St. 1–3, Tobias Clausnitzer, 1667
St. 4, author unknown, 1707
Tr., Catherine Winkworth, 1858

Johann R. Ahle, 1664

1 Bless-ed Je-sus, at Thy word We are gath-ered all to hear Thee; Let our hearts and souls be stirred Now to seek and love and fear Thee, By Thy teach-ings, sweet and ho-ly, Drawn from earth to love Thee sole-ly.

2
All our knowledge, sense and sight
   Lie in deepest darkness shrouded
Till Thy Spirit breaks our night
   With the beams of truth unclouded.
Thou alone to God canst win us;
Thou must work all good within us.

3
Glorious Lord, Thyself impart,
   Light of Light, from God proceed-
      ing;
Open Thou our ears and heart,
   Help us by Thy Spirit's pleading;
Hear the cry Thy people raises,
Hear and bless our prayers and
      praises.

4

Father, Son, and Holy Ghost,
Praise to Thee and adoration!
Grant that we Thy Word may trust
And obtain true consolation
While we here below must wander,
Till we sing Thy praises yonder.

78

Lord, This Day Thy Children Meet

Vienna—7. 7. 7. 7.

William W. How, 1823-1897   Justin H. Knecht, 1797

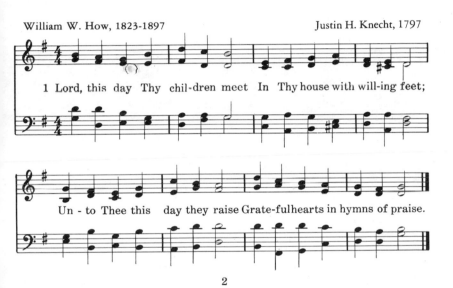

1 Lord, this day Thy chil-dren meet In Thy house with will-ing feet;

Un - to Thee this day they raise Grate-ful hearts in hymns of praise.

2

Help us unto Thee to pray,
Hallowing our happy day;
From Thy presence thus to win
Hearts all pure and free from sin.

3

All our pleasures here below,
Savior, from Thy mercy flow;
Little children Thou dost love;
Draw our hearts to Thee above.

4

Make, O Lord, our childhood shine
With all lowly grace, like Thine;
Then, through all eternity,
We shall live in heaven with Thee.

Lord Jesus Christ, Be Present Now

Herr Jesu Christ, dich—L. M.

Author unknown, 1651
Tr., Catherine Winkworth, 1863, alt.

"Cantionale Germanicum"
Dresden, 1628

1 Lord Jesus Christ, be pres-ent now, Our hearts in true de-vo-tion bow, Thy Spir-it send with grace di-vine, And let Thy truth with-in us shine.

2

Unseal our lips to sing Thy praise,
Our souls to Thee in worship raise,
Make strong our faith, increase our
      light
That we may know Thy name aright.

3

Until we join the hosts that cry,
"Holy art Thou, O Lord, most high!"
And in the light of that blest place
Fore'er behold Thee face to face.

4

Glory to God the Father, Son,
And Holy Spirit, Three in One!
To Thee, O blessed Trinity,
Be praise throughout eternity!

Thy Presence, Gracious God, Afford

Mendon—L. M.

John Fawcett, 1740-1817

German melody
Arr. by Samuel Dyer, 1828

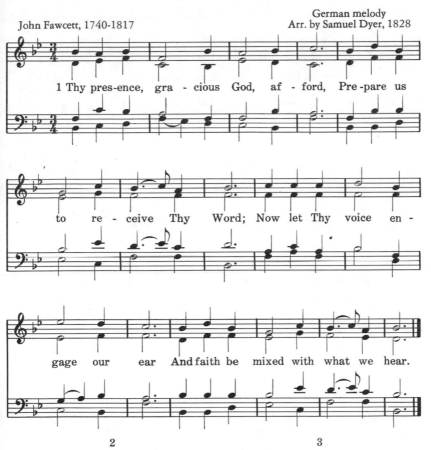

1 Thy pres-ence, gra - cious God, af - ford, Pre -pare us to re - ceive Thy Word; Now let Thy voice en - gage our ear And faith be mixed with what we hear.

2
Distracting thoughts and cares
    remove,
And fix our hearts and hopes above;
With food divine may we be fed
And satisfied with living bread.

3
To us the sacred Word apply
With mighty power and energy;
And may we, in Thy faith and fear,
Reduce to practice what we hear.

4
Father, in us Thy Son reveal,
Teach us to know and do Thy will,
Thy saving power and love display,
And guide us to the realms of day.

Assembled in Our School Once More

O heilige Dreifaltigkeit—L. M.

Author unknown

Nikolaus Herman, 1560

1 As - sem-bled in our school once more, O Lord, Thy bless - ing we im - plore; We meet to read and sing and pray; Be with us, then, through this Thy day.

2

Our fervent prayer to Thee ascends
For parents, teachers, and for friends;
And when we in Thy house appear,
Help us to worship in Thy fear.

3

When we on earth shall meet no more,
May we above to glory soar
And praise Thee in more lofty strains,
Where one eternal Sabbath reigns.

See also:

Holy Ghost, with Light Divine
Holy Spirit, Hear Us
Gracious Spirit, Dove Divine
Holy, Holy, Holy, Lord God Almighty
With the Lord Begin Thy Task

The Radiant Sun Shines in the Skies

Die helle Sonn' leucht't—L. M.

Nikolaus Herman, 1560
Tr., composite

Melchior Vulpius, 1609

1 The ra-diant sun shines in the skies, With joy from sleep we now a-rise. All praise to God, who through this night Hath kept us from the dev-il's might.

2
Lord Jesus Christ, guide us this day;
Keep sin and shame far from our
   way.
Thy guardian angels to us send,
And let them to our wants attend.

3
Direct our hearts to do Thy will,
And for Thy Word true love instill
That we may do whate'er is right
And ever pleasing in Thy sight.

4
Crown all our labors with success,
Each one in his own calling bless.
May all we do or think or say
Exalt and praise Thee, Lord, this day!

83

With the Lord Begin Thy Task

Fang dein Werk—7. 6. 7. 6. D., *Trochaic*

German author unknown, 1734
Tr., W. Gustave Polack, 1937, cento

Peter Frank, 1657

1 With the Lord be - gin thy task, Je - sus will di - rect it;

For His aid and coun - sel ask, Je - sus will per - fect it.

Ev - 'ry morn with Je - sus rise, And when day is end - ed,

In His name then close thine eyes; Be to Him com - mend - ed.

2

Let each day begin with prayer,
  Praise, and adoration;
On the Lord cast ev'ry care,
  He is thy Salvation.
Morning, evening, and at night
  Jesus will be near thee,
Save thee from the Tempter's might,
  With His presence cheer thee.

3

Thus, Lord Jesus, every task
  Be to Thee commended;
May Thy will be done, I ask,
  Until life is ended.
Jesus, in Thy name begun
  Be the day's endeavor;
Grant that it may well be done
  To Thy praise forever.

84

Now the Shades of Night Are Gone

Vienna—7. 7. 7. 7.

Samson Occom, †1792, asc.   Justin H. Knecht, 1797

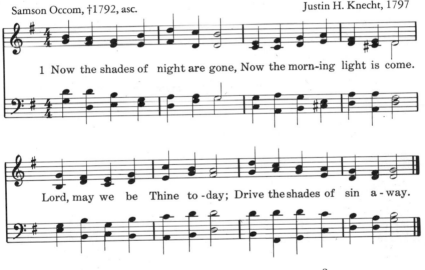

1 Now the shades of night are gone, Now the morn-ing light is come.

Lord, may we be Thine to-day; Drive the shades of sin a-way.

2

Fill our souls with heav'nly light,
Banish doubt and cleanse our sight.
In Thy service, Lord, today
Help us labor, help us pray.

3

Keep our haughty passions bound,
Save us from our foes around;
Going out and coming in,
Keep us safe from ev'ry sin.

4

When our work of life is past,
Oh, receive us then at last!
Night of sin will be no more
When we reach the heav'nly shore.

When Morning Gilds the Skies

Franconian Melody—6. 6. 6. 6. 6. 6.

From the German. Author unknown
Tr., Edward Caswell, 1814-1878. Ab.

Anon.

1 When morn-ing gilds the skies, My heart, a-wak-ing,
cries: May Je-sus Christ be praised! A - like at work and
pray'r To Je - sus I re - pair. May Je - sus
Christ be praised! May Je-sus Christ be praised!

2

The night becomes as day
When from the heart we say:
    May Jesus Christ be praised!
The pow'rs of darkness fear
When this sweet chant we hear:
    May Jesus Christ be praised!
    May Jesus Christ be praised!

3

In heav'n's eternal bliss
The loveliest strain is this:
    May Jesus Christ be praised!
Let earth and sea and sky
From depth to height reply:
    May Jesus Christ be praised!
    May Jesus Christ be praised!

4

Be this, while life is mine,
My canticle divine:
    May Jesus Christ be praised!
Be this th' eternal song
Through all the ages long:
    May Jesus Christ be praised!
    May Jesus Christ be praised!

86

Refreshed by Gentle Slumbers

Magdalena—7. 6. 7. 6.

Anon.

German traditional melody
(c. 16th century)

1 Re-freshed by gen-tle slum-bers, From care and sor-row free,

Our hearts in tune-ful num-bers Sing praise, O Lord, to Thee.

2

Thou spreadest joy and blessing,
    Thou Source of ev'ry good;
Then hear us, Thee addressing,
    In songs of gratitude.

3

Oh, may we, ceasing never,
    Extol Thee all our days;
Our heart and life be ever
    An endless song of praise!

Tune arrangement from *Songs of Praise.* Copyright, Oxford University Press.
Used by permission.

O Blessed Holy Trinity

O heilige Dreifaltigkeit—L. M.

Martin Behm, 1608, ab.
Tr., Conrad H. L. Schuette, 1880, alt.

Nikolaus Herman, 1560

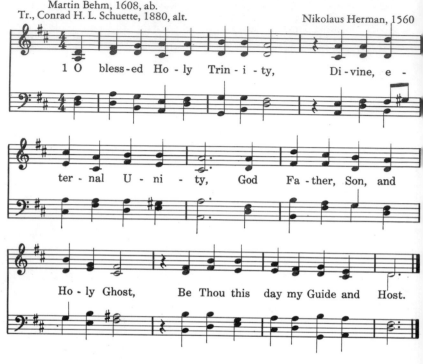

1 O bless-ed Ho-ly Trin-i-ty, Di-vine, e-ter-nal U-ni-ty, God Fa-ther, Son, and Ho-ly Ghost, Be Thou this day my Guide and Host.

2

My soul and body keep from harm,
O'er all I have extend Thine arm,
That Satan may not cause distress
Nor bring me shame and
    wretchedness.

3

The Father's love shield me this day,
The Son's pure wisdom cheer my way,
The Holy Spirit's light divine
Illume my heart's benighted shrine.

4

My Maker, strengthen Thou my heart,
O my Redeemer, help impart,
Blest Comforter, keep at my side
That faith and love in me abide.

5

Lord, bless and keep Thou me as
    Thine;
Lord, make Thy face upon me shine;
Lord, lift Thy countenance on me,
And give me peace, sweet peace,
    from Thee.

See also:

    Holy Ghost, with Light Divine
    Gracious Spirit, Dove Divine
    Holy, Holy, Holy, Lord God Almighty
    Glory Be to God the Father
    Hymns of Worship and Praise

Savior, Again to Thy Dear Name We Raise

Ellers—10. 10. 10. 10.

John Ellerton, 1866 · Edward J. Hopkins, 1869

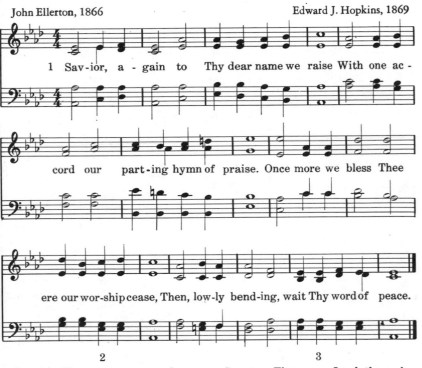

1 Sav-ior, a-gain to Thy dear name we raise With one ac-cord our part-ing hymn of praise. Once more we bless Thee ere our wor-ship cease, Then, low-ly bend-ing, wait Thy word of peace.

2
Grant us Thy peace upon our home-
ward way;
With Thee began, with Thee shall
end, the day.
Guard Thou the lips from sin, the
hearts from shame,
That in this house have called upon
Thy name.

3
Grant us Thy peace, Lord, through
the coming night;
Turn Thou for us its darkness into
light.
From harm and danger keep Thy
children free;
For dark and light are both alike
to Thee.

God Be with You Till We Meet Again

Randolph—9. 8. 8. 9.

J. E. Rankin, 1828-1904   Ralph Vaughan Williams, b. 1872

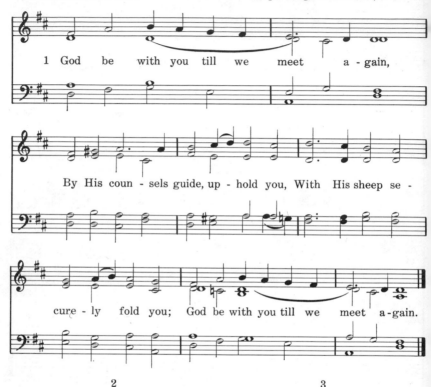

1 God be with you till we meet a - gain,

By His coun - sels guide, up - hold you, With His sheep se -

cure - ly fold you; God be with you till we meet a - gain.

2

God be with you till we meet again,
  'Neath His wings protecting hide
    you,
  Daily manna still provide you;
God be with you till we meet again.

3

God be with you till we meet again,
  When life's perils thick confound
    you,
  Put His arm unfailing round you;
God be with you till we meet again.

4

God be with you till we meet again,
  Keep love's banner floating o'er you,
  Smite death's threat'ning wave
    before you;
God be with you till we meet again.

Tune from *The English Hymnal.* Copyright 1906 by the English Hymnal Committee.
Used by permission of Oxford University Press.

Once More, Before We Part

St. Michael—S. M.

Author unknown

"Genevan Psalter," 1551

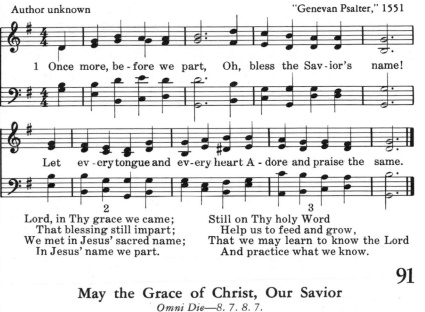

1 Once more, be-fore we part, Oh, bless the Sav-ior's name!

Let ev-ery tongue and ev-ery heart A - dore and praise the same.

2
Lord, in Thy grace we came;
That blessing still impart;
We met in Jesus' sacred name;
In Jesus' name we part.

3
Still on Thy holy Word
Help us to feed and grow,
That we may learn to know the Lord
And practice what we know.

91

May the Grace of Christ, Our Savior

Omni Die—8. 7. 8. 7.

John Newton, 1725-1807

Melody in Corner's Gesangbuch, 1631
Harm. by William Smith Rockstro, 1823-1895

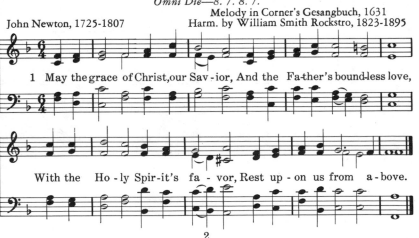

1 May the grace of Christ, our Sav-ior, And the Fa-ther's bound-less love,

With the Ho-ly Spir-it's fa - vor, Rest up-on us from a-bove.

2
Thus may we abide in union
With each other and the Lord,
And possess, in sweet communion,
Joys which earth cannot afford.

92

Lord, Dismiss Us with Thy Blessing

Regent Square—8. 7. 8. 7. 8. 7.

John Fawcett, 1773

Henry Smart, 1867

1 Lord, dis-miss us with Thy bless-ing, Fill our hearts with joy and peace. Let us each, Thy love pos-sess-ing, Tri-umph in re - deem-ing grace. Oh, re-fresh us, Oh, re-fresh us, Trav-'ling through this wil - der-ness!

2

Thanks we give and adoration
For Thy Gospel's joyful sound.
May the fruits of Thy salvation
In our hearts and lives abound;
Ever faithful, Ever faithful
To the Truth may we be found!

Let Thy Blessing Now Attend Us

Hyfrydol—8. 7. 8. 7. D.

Author unknown

Rowland N. Prichard, 1811-1887

1 Let Thy bless-ing now at-tend us, Lov-ing Sav-ior, to each home;

From all dan-ger Thou de-fend us, Till a-gain we hith-er come.

With Thy rod and staff be near us Lest we fol-low ways of sin;

With Thy gra-cious pres-ence cheer us, Cleanse our hearts and dwell there-in.

2

Make us patient, meek, and lowly,
 Make us shun the ways of strife;
Keep us in the path of duty,
 Steadfast in the Christian life.
Thus we'd follow Thee, dear Savior,
 Till we've crossed life's stormy sea
And with all Thy faithful children
 Thou dost call us home to Thee.

Almighty Father, Bless the Word

Old Hundredth—L. M.

Author unknown

"Genevan Psalter," 1551

1 Al - might-y Fa-ther, bless the Word Which through Thy grace we now have heard. Oh, may the pre-cious seed take root, Spring up, and bear a - bun - dant fruit!

2

We praise Thee for the means of
    grace
As homeward now our steps we trace.
Grant, Lord, that we who worship
    here
May all at last in heav'n appear.

See also:
    Glory to the Father Give
    Glory Be to God the Father
    Abide, O Dearest Jesus

All Praise to Thee, My God, This Night

Tallis' Canon—L. M.

Thomas Ken, 1695, cento   Thomas Tallis, c. 1567

1 All praise to Thee, my God, this night For all the bless-ings of the light. Keep me, oh, keep me, King of Kings, Be-neath Thine own al-might-y wings.

2

Forgive me, Lord, for Thy dear Son,
The ill that I this day have done
That with the world, myself, and
    Thee
I, ere I sleep, at peace may be.

3

Teach me to live that I may dread
The grave as little as my bed.
Teach me to die that so I may
Rise glorious at the awe-full Day.

4

Oh, may my soul on Thee repose,
And may sweet sleep mine eyelids
    close,
Sleep that shall me more vigorous
    make
To serve my God when I awake!

5

When in the night I sleepless lie,
My soul with heavenly thoughts
    supply;
Let no ill dreams disturb my rest,
No power of darkness me molest.

6

Praise God, from whom all blessings
    flow;
Praise Him, all creatures here below;
Praise Him above, ye heavenly host;
Praise Father, Son, and Holy Ghost.

96

Now the Light Has Gone Away

Muede bin ich—7. 7. 7. 7.

Frances R. Havergal, 1869

"Liederbuch fuer Kleinkinder-Schulen"
Kaiserswerth, 1842

1 Now the light has gone a - way; Fa-ther, lis-ten while I pray,

Ask-ing Thee to watch and keep And to send me qui-et sleep.

2
Jesus, Savior, wash away
All that has been wrong today;
Help me ev'ry day to be
Good and gentle, more like Thee.

3
Let my near and dear ones be
Always near and dear to Thee;
Oh, bring me and all I love
To Thy happy home above.

4
Now my evening praise I give;
Thou didst die that I might live.
All my blessings come from Thee,
Oh, how good Thou art to me!

5
Thou, my best and kindest Friend,
Thou wilt love me to the end.
Let me love Thee more and more,
Always better than before.

Now Rest Beneath Night's Shadow

O Welt, ich muss dich lassen—7. 7. 6. 7. 7. 8.

Paul Gerhardt, 1648, cento
Tr., composite

Heinrich Isaak, c. 1490

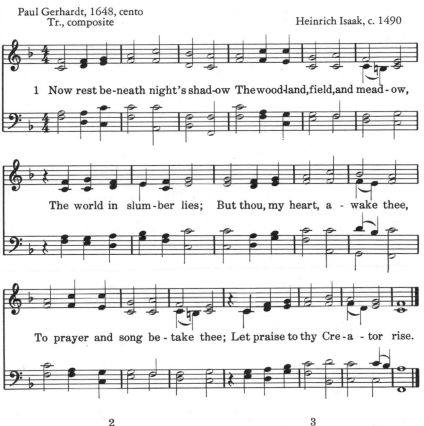

1 Now rest be-neath night's shad-ow The wood-land, field, and mead-ow,

The world in slum-ber lies; But thou, my heart, a - wake thee,

To prayer and song be - take thee; Let praise to thy Cre-a - tor rise.

2

Lord Jesus, who dost love me,
Oh, spread Thy wings above me
  And shield me from alarm!
Though evil would assail me,
Thy mercy will not fail me;
  I rest in Thy protecting arm.

3

My loved ones, rest securely,
For God this night will surely
  From peril guard your heads.
Sweet slumbers may He send you
And bid His hosts attend you
  And through the night watch o'er
    your beds.

Now the Day Is Over

Eudoxia—6. 5. 6. 5.

Sabine Baring-Gould, 1865   Sabine Baring-Gould, 1865

1 Now the day is o - ver, Night is draw-ing nigh;

Shad-ows of the eve - ning Steal a - cross the sky.

2
Now the darkness gathers,
    Stars begin to peep,
Birds and beasts and flowers
    Soon will be asleep.

3
Jesus, give the weary
    Calm and sweet repose;
With Thy tend'rest blessing
    May mine eyelids close.

4
Grant to little children
    Visions bright of Thee;
Guard the sailors tossing
    On the deep-blue sea.

5
Comfort every sufferer
    Watching late in pain;
Those who plan some evil
    From their sin restrain.

6
Through the long night watches
    May Thine angels spread
Their white wings above me,
    Watching round my bed.

7
When the morning wakens,
    Then may I arise
Pure and fresh and sinless
    In Thy holy eyes.

8
Glory to the Father,
    Glory to the Son,
And to Thee, blest Spirit,
    While all ages run.

See also:

O Christ, Thou Lamb of God
We All Believe in One True God
May the Grace of Christ, Our Savior
Oh, Bless the Lord, My Soul
Savior, Like a Shepherd Lead Us

Jesus, Lover of My Soul
The Lord's My Shepherd, I'll Not Want
I Am Trusting Thee, Lord Jesus
Rock of Ages, Cleft for Me
He Cares for Me

Sing to the Lord of Harvest

Wie lieblich ist der Maien—7. 6. 7. 6. D.

J. S. B. Monsell, 1811 - 1875

"Himmlische Harpffe Davids"
Nuernberg, 1581

1 Sing to the Lord of har-vest, Sing songs of love and praise;
With joy - ful hearts and voi - ces Your al - le - lu - ias raise!
By Him the roll - ing sea - sons In fruit-ful or - der move;
Sing to the Lord of har - vest A song of hap - py love.

2	3
By Him the clouds drop fatness, The deserts bloom and spring, The hills leap up in gladness, The valleys laugh and sing. He filleth with His fullness All things with large increase; He crowns the year with goodness, With plenty, and with peace.	Heap on His sacred altar The gifts His goodness gave, The golden sheaves of harvest, The souls He died to save. Your hearts lay down before Him When at His feet ye fall, And with your lives adore Him Who gave His life for all.

We Plow the Fields and Scatter

Wir pfluegen—7. 6. 7. 6. D., with Refrain

Matthias Claudius, 1740-1815
Tr., Jane M. Campbell, 1817-1878   Johann A. P. Schulz, 1747-1800

1 We plow the fields and scat-ter The good seed on the land,

But it is fed and wa-tered By God's al-might-y hand;

He sends the snow in win-ter, The warmth to swell the grain,

The breez-es and the sun-shine, And soft, re-fresh-ing rain.

Refrain

All good gifts a - round us Are sent from heaven a - bove;

Then thank the Lord, oh, thank the Lord For all His love.

2

He only is the Maker
 Of all things near and far;
He paints the wayside flower,
 He lights the evening star;
The winds and waves obey Him,
 By Him the birds are fed;
Much more to us, His children,
 He gives our daily bread.

3

We thank Thee, then, O Father,
 For all things bright and good,
The seedtime and the harvest,
 Our life, our health, our food;
No gifts have we to offer,
 For all Thy love imparts,
But that which Thou desirest,
 Our humble, thankful hearts.

Refrain:
All good gifts around us
 Are sent from heaven above;
Then thank the Lord, oh, thank the Lord
 For all His love.

Come, Ye Thankful People, Come

St. George—7. 7. 7. 7. D.

Henry Alford, 1844, cento, alt.　　　　　　　　　　　George J. Elvey, 1858

1 Come, ye thank-ful peo-ple, come; Raise the song of har-vest home.

All be safe-ly gath-ered in Ere the win-ter storms be-gin;

God, our Mak-er, doth pro-vide For our wants to be sup-plied.

Come to God's own tem-ple, come; Raise the song of har-vest home.

2
All the world is God's own field,
Fruit unto His praise to yield;
Wheat and tares together sown,
Unto joy or sorrow grown;
First the blade and then the ear,
Then the full corn shall appear.
Lord of harvest, grant that we
Wholesome grain and pure may be.

3
For the Lord, our God, shall come
And shall take His harvest home;
From His field shall in that day
All offenses purge away;
Give His angels charge at last
In the fire the tares to cast,
But the fruitful ears to store
In His garner evermore.

4

Even so, Lord, quickly come
To Thy final harvest home;
Gather Thou Thy people in,
Free from sorrow, free from sin,
There, forever purified,
In Thy garner to abide.
Come with all Thine angels, come,
Raise the glorious harvest home.

102

God Hath Given Us Harvest

St. Lucian—6. 5. 6. 5.

J. A. Davies

Joh. Christoph Heinrich Rinck, 1770-1846

1 God hath giv'n us har-vest, Let us praise His name;

While the earth re - main - eth, He is still the same.

2

Year by year His promise
    Faithfully endures;
Seedtime, sunshine, harvest,
    He for men insures.

3

Rain from heav'n He sendeth
    On the growing grain;
Fruitful seasons gives us;
    Goodness is His name.

4

Glory, then, forever
    Be to Father, Son,
With the Holy Spirit,
    Blessed Three in One.

We Praise Thee, O God, Our Redeemer, Creator

Kremser—12. 11. 12. 11.

Author unknown, 1626
Tr., Julia B. Cady Cory, 1902

"Nederlandtsch Gedenckclanck"
Haarlem, 1626

1 We praise Thee, O God, our Re-deem-er, Cre-a-tor,

In grate-ful de-vo-tion our trib-ute we bring;

We lay it be-fore Thee, we kneel and a-dore Thee,

We bless Thy ho-ly name, glad prais-es we sing.

2
We worship Thee, God of our fathers,
　　we bless Thee;
　Through life's storm and tempest
　　our Guide hast Thou been;
When perils o'ertake us, escape Thou
　　wilt make us,
　And with Thy help, O Lord, our
　　battles we win.

3
With voices united our praises we
　　offer,
　To Thee, great Jehovah, glad
　　anthems we raise.
Thy strong arm will guide us, our
　　God is beside us,
　To Thee, our great Redeemer,
　　fore'er be praise.

A Glad and Happy Birthday

Ellacombe—6. 6. 7. 6. D.

Author unknown

"Gesangbuch d. Herzogl.
Wuerttemberg. Hofkapelle," 1784

A glad and hap-py birth-day We wish to you, our friend,

And may our heav'n-ly Fa - ther A birth-day bless-ing send.

A hap-py, hap-py birth-day, All beau-ti-ful with love

And bright with man-y bless-ings From our dear Lord a - bove.

105

O Father, Bless These Children Dear

O Jesulein suess—8. 8. 8. 8. 8.

Edith F. B. MacAlister, alt.   Melody from S. Scheidt's Tabulaturbuch, 1650

O Fa - ther, bless these chil - dren dear, And keep them happy all the year; May they be strong in faith and true And do as Thou would'st have them do; O Je - sus, bless these chil - dren too.

See also:

Oh, that the Lord Would Guide My Ways
Take My Life and Let It Be
O Jesus, I Have Promised
I Walk with Jesus All the Way
Thine Forever, God of Love

For Food and Drink

Old Hundredth—L. M.

Isaac Watts, 1674-1748
St. 2 anon.

"Genevan Psalter," 1551

Before Meals
Be present at our table, Lord;
Be here and everywhere adored.
Thy children bless, and grant that we
May feast in Paradise with Thee.
    Amen.

After Meals
For food and drink and happy days
Accept our gratitude and praise;
In serving others, Lord, may we
Repay in part our debt to Thee.
    Amen.

There Is a Name I Love to Hear

Lobt Gott, ihr Christen—C. M.

Frederick Whitfield, 1829-1904, alt.

Nikolaus Herman, 1554

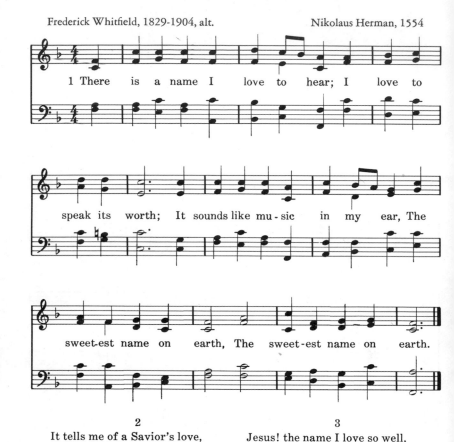

1 There is a name I love to hear; I love to speak its worth; It sounds like music in my ear, The sweet-est name on earth, The sweet-est name on earth.

2
It tells me of a Savior's love,
Who died to set me free;
It tells me of His precious blood,
The blood He shed for me.

3
Jesus! the name I love so well,
The name I love to hear;
No saint on earth its worth can tell,
No heart can know how dear.

See also:
How Sweet the Name of Jesus Sounds
Jesus, the Very Thought of Thee
Jesus, Jesus, Only Jesus
I Walk with Jesus All the Way
Our God, Our Help in Ages Past

Come, Ye Children, Praise the Savior

Jesus, Jesus, nichts als Jesus—8. 7. 8. 7. 7. 7.

Anon., alt.
Bible Class Magazine, 1851   "Vollkommenes Choralbuch," Hamburg, 1715

1 Come, ye children, praise the Savior; He regards you from above;
Praise Him for His great salvation; Praise Him for His precious love.
Sweet hosannas loudly sing To your Savior and your King.

2
When the anxious mothers round Him
  With their tender infants pressed,
He with open arms received them,
  And the little ones He blessed.
Sweet hosannas loudly sing
To your Savior and your King.

3
Up in yonder happy regions
  Angels sound the chorus high;
Twice ten thousand times ten thousand
  Send His praises through the sky.
Sweet hosannas loudly sing
To your Savior and your King.

Oh, that I Had a Thousand Voices

O dass ich tausend—9. 8. 9. 8. 8. 8.

Johann Mentzer, 1704, cento
Tr., composite

Johann B. Koenig, 1738

1 Oh, that I had a thou-sand voic - es To praise my God with thou-sand tongues! My heart, which in the Lord re - joic - es, Would then pro - claim in grate - ful songs To all, wher - ev - er I might be, What great things God hath done for me.

2

All creatures that have breath and motion,
  That throng the earth, the sea, and sky,
Now join me in my heart's devotion,
  Help me to raise His praises high.
My utmost pow'rs can ne'er aright
Declare the wonders of His might.

3

Lord, I will tell, while I am living,
  Thy goodness forth with every breath
And greet each morning with thanks-giving
  Until my heart is still in death;
Yea, when at last my lips grow cold,
Thy praise shall in my sighs be told.

Praise to the Lord, the Almighty

Lobe den Herren, den—14. 14. 4. 7. 8.

Joachim Neander, 1679, cento
Tr., Catherine Winkworth, 1863, alt.

"Erneuertes Gesangbuch"
Stralsund, 1665

1 Praise to the Lord, the Al-might-y, the King of cre-a- - tion! O my soul, praise Him, for He is thy Health and Sal-va- - tion! Join the full throng; Wake, harp and psal-ter and song; Sound forth in glad ad-o-ra- - tion!

2
Praise to the Lord, who o'er all
   things so wondrously reigneth,
Who, as on wings of an eagle, up-
   lifteth, sustaineth.
  Hast thou not seen
  How thy desires all have been
Granted in what He ordaineth?

3
Praise to the Lord! Oh, let all that is
   in me adore Him!
All that hath life and breath, come
   now with praises before Him!
  Let the Amen
  Sound from His people again;
Gladly for aye we adore Him.

111

All Praise to God, Who Reigns Above

Lobet den Herrn, ihr—8. 7. 8. 7.8. 8. 7.

Johann J. Schuetz, 1675, cento
Tr., composite

Melchior Vulpius, 1609

1 All praise to God, who reigns a - bove, The God of
all cre - a - tion, The God of won - ders, pow'r, and
love, The God of our sal - va - tion! With heal -ing
balm my soul He fills, The God who ev - 'ry
sor - row stills – To God all praise and glo - ry!

2

What God's almighty power hath
   made
His gracious mercy keepeth;
By morning dawn or evening shade
His watchful eye ne'er sleepeth;
Within the kingdom of His might,
Lo, all is just and all is right—
   To God all praise and glory!

3

I cried to Him in time of need:
   Lord God, oh, hear my calling!
For death He gave me life indeed
   And kept my feet from falling.
For this my thanks shall endless be;
Oh, thank Him, thank our God, with
   me—
   To God all praise and glory!

4

Then come before His presence now
   And banish fear and sadness;
To your Redeemer pay your vow
   And sing with joy and gladness:
Though great distress my soul befell,
The Lord, my God, did all things
   well—
   To God all praise and glory!

112

Endless Praises to Our Lord

Culbach—7. 7. 7. 7.

Thomas Kelly, 1769-1854

"Heilige Seelenlust"
Breslau, 1657, ad.

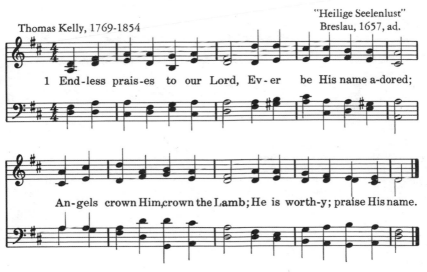

1 End-less prais-es to our Lord, Ev-er be His name a-dored;

An-gels crown Him, crown the Lamb; He is worth-y; praise His name.

2

Now adore Him for His grace
To our guilty, fallen race;
Come, then, children, join to sing:
"Glory to our God, the King."

For the Beauty of the Earth

Dix—7. 7. 7. 7. 7. 7.

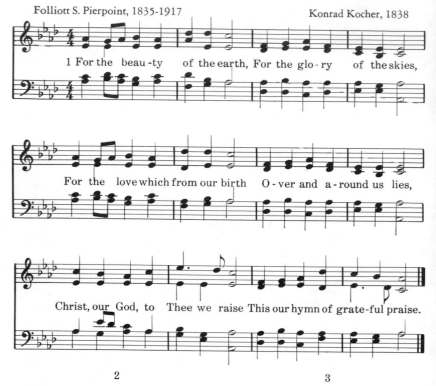

Folliott S. Pierpoint, 1835-1917

Konrad Kocher, 1838

1 For the beau-ty of the earth, For the glo-ry of the skies,
For the love which from our birth O-ver and a-round us lies,
Christ, our God, to Thee we raise This our hymn of grate-ful praise.

2
For the wonder of each hour
 Of the day and of the night,
Hill and vale, and tree and flow'r,
 Sun and moon, and stars of light,
Christ, our God, to Thee we raise
This our hymn of grateful praise.

3
For the joy of human love,
 Brother, sister, parent, child,
Friends on earth and friends above,
 For all gentle thoughts and mild,
Christ, our God, to Thee we raise
This our hymn of grateful praise.

4
For Thy Church that evermore
 Lifteth holy hands above,
Off'ring up on ev'ry shore
 Her pure sacrifice of love,
Christ, our Lord, to Thee we raise
This our hymn of grateful praise.

Come, Praise Your Lord and Savior

Freut euch, ihr lieben—7. 6. 7. 6. D.

William W. How, 1823-1897

Leonhart Schroeter, 1587

1 Come, praise your Lord and Sav - ior In songs of ho - ly mirth!
Give thanks to Him, O chil - dren, Who lived a child on earth!
He loved the lit - tle chil - dren And called them to His side,
His lov-ing arms em-braced them, And for their sins He died.

2
O Jesus, we would praise Thee
  With songs of holy joy;
For Thou on earth didst sojourn,
  A pure and spotless boy.
Make us like Thee, obedient,
  Like Thee from sin stains free;
Like Thee in God's own temple,
  In lowly home like Thee.

3
O Lord, with voices lifted·
  We sing our songs of praise;
Be Thou the light and pattern·
  Of all our childhood days;
And lead us ever onward,
  That while we stay below,
We may, like Thee, O Jesus,
  In grace and wisdom grow.

Dear Lord, While We Adoring Pay

Adoration — 8. 6. 8. 6. 6.

Author unknown   Richard T. Rohlfing, 1953

1 Dear Lord, while we, a - dor - ing, pay Our hum-ble thanks to Thee, May ev - 'ry heart with rap - ture say: "The Sav - ior died for me!" "The Sav - ior died for me!"

2
Oh, may the sweet, the blissful theme
Fill ev'ry heart and tongue
Till strangers love the charming name
And join the happy throng,
And join the happy throng.

From *Echoes from Bethlehem.* Copyright 1954 by Concordia Publishing House

Oh, Bless the Lord, My Soul

St. Thomas—S. M.

Isaac Watts, 1719

Aaron Williams, 1770

1 Oh, bless the Lord, my soul! Let all with-in me join
And aid my tongue to bless His name Whose fa-vors are di - vine.

2

Oh, bless the Lord, my soul,
　Nor let His mercies lie
Forgotten in unthankfulness
　And without praises die!

3

'Tis He forgives thy sins;
　'Tis He relieves thy pain;
'Tis He that heals thy sicknesses
　And makes thee young again.

4

He crowns thy life with love
　When ransomed from the grave;
He that redeemed my soul from hell
　Hath sov'reign pow'r to save.

5

He fills the poor with good;
　He gives the sufferers rest:
The Lord hath judgments for the
　　proud
　And justice for th' opprest.

6

His wondrous works and ways
　He made by Moses known,
But sent the world His truth and
　　grace
　By His beloved Son.

Now Thank We All Our God

Nun danket alle Gott—6. 7. 6. 7. 6. 6. 6. 6.

Martin Rinckart, 1636
Tr., Catherine Winkworth, 1858

Johann Crueger, 1648

1 Now thank we all our God With heart and hands and voic-es,

Who won-drous things hath done, In whom His world re-joic-es;

Who from our moth-er's arms Hath blessed us on our way

With count-less gifts of love, And still is ours to-day.

2
Oh, may this bounteous God
　Through all our life be near us,
With ever joyful hearts
　And blessed peace to cheer us;
And keep us in His grace
　And guide us when perplexed
And free us from all ills
　In this world and the next!

3
All praise and thanks to God
　The Father now be given,
The Son, and Him who reigns
　With them in highest heaven:
The one eternal God,
　Whom earth and heav'n adore!
For thus it was, is now,
　And shall be evermore.

Singing for Jesus

Slane—10. 10. 10. 10.

Emmanuel Poppen, 1935

Ancient Irish traditional melody
Harm. by David Evans, 1874-1948

1 Sing-ing for Je-sus, our Sav-ior and King,

Sing-ing for Je-sus, the Lord whom we love;

All ad-o-ra-tion we joy-ous-ly bring,

Long-ing to praise as they praise Him a-bove.

2
Singing for Jesus, our Shepherd and
    Guide,
    Singing for gladness of heart that
    He gives;
Singing for wonder and praise that
    He died,
    Singing for blessing and joy that
    He lives.

3
Singing for Jesus, yes, singing for
    joy,
    Thus will we praise Him and tell
    out His love;
Till He shall call us to brighter
    employ,
    Singing for Jesus, forever above.

Words used by permission of the Wartburg Press. Harmony from *The Church Hymnary, revised.* Copyright 1927 by Oxford University Press. Used by permission.

119

We Thank Thee, Loving Father

Maria ist geboren—7. 6. 7. 6.

Author unknown

Coeln (Brachel, 1623)
Harm. by Charles Wood

1 We thank Thee, lov - ing Fa - ther, For all Thy ten - der care, For food and clothes and shel - ter And all the world so fair.

2
Oh, give us hearts to thank Thee
For ev'ry blessing sent,
And whatsoe'er Thou sendest,
Make us therewith content.

Harmonization from G. R. Woodward's *Songs of Syon.* Copyright by Schott and Co., London, England. Used by permission.

See also:
When Morning Gilds the Skies
Oh, for a Thousand Tongues to Sing
From All That Dwell Below the Skies
When All Thy Mercies, O My God
All Glory Be to God on High
Children of the Heavenly King

All Hail the Power of Jesus' Name

Coronation—C. M.

Edward Perronet, 1779, cento, alt.

Oliver Holden, 1793

1 All hail the pow'r of Je-sus' name! Let an-gels pros-trate fall;

Bring forth the roy-al di - a - dem And crown Him Lord of all.

Bring forth the roy-al di - a - dem And crown Him Lord of all.

2

Ye seed of Israel's chosen race,
　Ye ransomed from the Fall,
Hail Him who saves you by His grace
　And crown Him Lord of all.
Hail Him who saves you by His grace
　And crown Him Lord of all.

3

Let every kindred, every tribe,
　On this terrestrial ball
To Him all majesty ascribe
　And crown Him Lord of all.
To Him all majesty ascribe
　And crown Him Lord of all.

4

Oh, that with yonder sacred throng
　We at His feet may fall!
We'll join the everlasting song
　And crown Him Lord of all.
We'll join the everlasting song
　And crown Him Lord of all.

121

Oh, for a Thousand Tongues to Sing

Beatitudo—C. M.

Charles Wesley, 1739   John B. Dykes, 1875

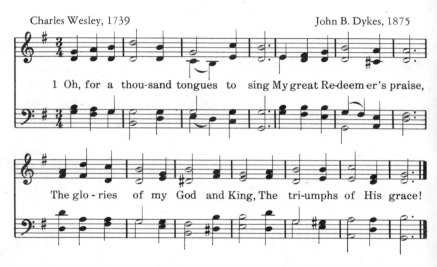

1 Oh, for a thou-sand tongues to sing My great Re-deem-er's praise,

The glo - ries of my God and King, The tri-umphs of His grace!

2

My gracious Master and my God,
  Assist me to proclaim,
To spread through all the earth abroad,
  The honors of Thy name.

3

Jesus! the name that charms our fears,
  That bids our sorrows cease;
'Tis music in the sinner's ears,
  'Tis life and health and peace.

4

He breaks the power of canceled sin,
  He sets the prisoner free;
His blood can make the foulest clean;
  His blood avails for me.

5

Look unto Him, ye nations; own
  Your God, ye fallen race.
Look and be saved through faith alone,
  Be justified by grace.

6

See all your sins on Jesus laid;
  The Lamb of God was slain;
His soul was once an offering made
  For every soul of man.

7

Glory to God and praise and love
  Be ever, ever given
By saints below and saints above,
  The Church in earth and heaven.

Crown Him with Many Crowns

Diademata—S. M. D.

Matthew Bridges, 1851, cento, alt.   George J. Elvey, 1868

1 Crown Him with man-y crowns, The Lamb up-on His throne,

Hark how the heav'n-ly an-them drowns All mu-sic but its own.

A-wake, my soul, and sing Of Him who died for thee,

And hail Him as thy match-less King Through all e-ter-ni-ty.

2
Crown Him the Lord of Life
  Who triumphed o'er the grave
And rose victorious in the strife
  For those He came to save.
His glories now we sing
  Who died and rose on high,
Who died eternal life to bring
  And lives that death may die.

3
Crown Him the Lord of heaven
  Enthroned in worlds above,
Crown Him the King to whom is given
  The wondrous name of Love.
Crown Him with many crowns
  As thrones before Him fall;
Crown Him, ye kings, with many
  crowns,
    For He is King of all.

Jesus, Lover of My Soul

First Tune—Aberystwyth—7. 7. 7. 7. D.

Charles Wesley, 1740

Joseph Parry, 1841-1903

1 Jesus, Lover of my soul, Let me to Thy bosom fly
While the nearer waters roll, While the tempest still is high.
Hide me, O my Savior, hide, Till the storm of life is past;
Safe into the haven guide. Oh, receive my soul at last!

2
Other refuge have I none;
  Hangs my helpless soul on Thee.
Leave, ah, leave me not alone,
  Still support and comfort me!
All my trust on Thee is stayed,
  All my help from Thee I bring;
Cover my defenseless head
  With the shadow of Thy wing.

3
Thou, O Christ, art all I want;
  More than all in Thee I find.
Raise the fallen, cheer the faint,
  Heal the sick, and lead the blind.
Just and holy is Thy name;
  I am all unrighteousness,
False and full of sin I am;
  Thou art full of truth and grace.

4

Plenteous grace with Thee is found,
 Grace to cover all my sin.
Let the healing streams abound;
 Make and keep me pure within.
Thou of life the Fountain art,
 Freely let me take of Thee:
Spring Thou up within my heart,
 Rise to all eternity.

Jesus, Lover of My Soul

Second Tune—Martyn—7. 7. 7. 7. D.

Charles Wesley, 1740   Simeon B. Marsh, 1834

1 Je-sus, Lov-er of my soul, Let me to Thy bos-om fly

While the near-er wa-ters roll, While the tem-pest still is high.

Hide me, O my Sav-ior, hide, Till the storm of life is past;

Safe in-to the ha-ven guide. Oh, re-ceive my soul at last!

124

O Kind and Gentle Savior

Freut euch, ihr lieben—7. 6. 7. 6. D.

Author unknown

Leonhart Schroeter, 1587

1 O kind and gen-tle Sav-ior, Who art the chil-dren's Friend,
We pray Thee now re-ceive us, Thy bless-ing on us send.
Our joys and all our sor-rows Thou will-est we should bring
And lay them all be-fore Thee, Our good and gra-cious King.

2

To Thee of old their children
The people came and brought;
From Thee Thy grace and favor
For little ones they sought;
And Thou didst not forbid them,
For Thou art good and kind;
In Thee a loving Savior
May we, Thy children, find.

3

Let not our ways and doings
Dishonor Thy dear name,
Nor words, nor deeds of evil
Our Christian calling shame.
Grant us Thy grace that boldly
We may our Lord confess;
While for the gifts Thou givest
Thy holy name we bless.

I Need Thee, Precious Jesus

Llangloffan—7. 6. 7. 6. D.

Frederick Whitfield, 1855

Welsh hymn melody

1 I need Thee, pre-cious Je - sus, For I am full of sin;

My soul is dark and guilt - y, My heart is dead with - in.

I need the cleans-ing foun-tain Where I can al-ways flee,

The blood of Christ most pre - cious, The sin-ner's per-fect plea.

2
I need Thee, precious Jesus,
For I am very poor;
A stranger and a pilgrim,
I have no earthly store.
I need the love of Jesus
To cheer me on my way,
To guide my doubting footsteps,
To be my strength and stay.

3
I need Thee, precious Jesus,
I need a Friend like Thee,
A Friend to soothe and pity,
A Friend to care for me.
I need the heart of Jesus
To feel each anxious care,
To tell my every trouble
And all my sorrow share.

126

Savior, Like a Shepherd Lead Us

Picardy—8. 7. 8. 7. 8. 7.

Dorothy Ann Thrupp, 1779-1847   French traditional melody

1 Sav-ior, like a shep-herd lead us, Much we need Thy ten-der care;

In Thy pleas-ant pas-tures feed us, For our use Thy folds pre - pare.

Bless-ed Je-sus, Bless-ed Je - sus, Thou hast bought us; Thine we are.

2

We are Thine; do Thou befriend us,
　Be the Guardian of our way;
Keep Thy flock, from sin defend us,
　Seek us when we go astray.
Blessed Jesus, Blessed Jesus,
　Hear us children when we pray.

3

Thou hast promised to receive us,
　Poor and sinful though we be;
Thou hast mercy to relieve us,
　Grace to cleanse, and power to free.
Blessed Jesus, Blessed Jesus,
　Let us early turn to Thee.

4

Early let us seek Thy favor,
　Early let us do Thy will;
Blessed Lord and only Savior,
　With Thy love our spirit fill.
Blessed Jesus, Blessed Jesus,
　Thou hast loved us, love us still.

127

How Sweet the Name of Jesus Sounds

St. Peter—C. M.

John Newton, 1779, cento

Alexander R. Reinagle, 1836

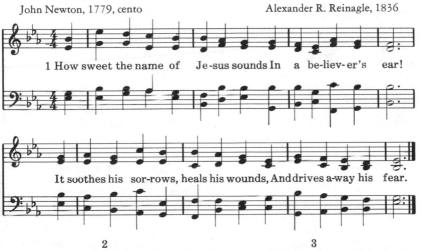

1 How sweet the name of Jesus sounds In a believ-er's ear!
It soothes his sorrows, heals his wounds, And drives away his fear.

2

It makes the wounded spirit whole
　And calms the troubled breast;
'Tis manna to the hungry soul
　And to the weary, rest.

3

Dear name! The Rock on which I build,
　My Shield and Hiding-place;
My never-failing Treas'ry, filled
　With boundless stores of grace.

4

Jesus, my Shepherd, Guardian, Friend,
　My Prophet, Priest, and King,
My Lord, my Life, my Way, my End,
　Accept the praise I bring.

128

Jesus, the Very Thought of Thee

Clairvaux—C. M.

Author unknown, 11th century, cento
Tr., Edward Caswall, 1849, alt.

Herman A. Polack, 1910

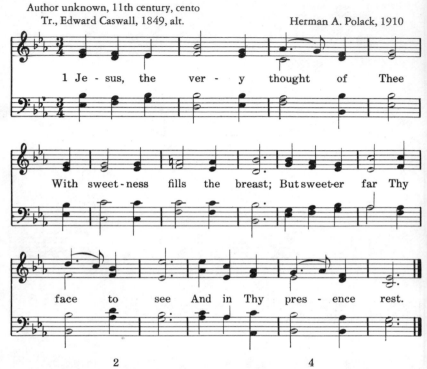

1 Je - sus, the ver - y thought of Thee
With sweet - ness fills the breast; But sweet-er far Thy
face to see And in Thy pres - ence rest.

2

Nor voice can sing, nor heart can
frame,
Nor can the mem'ry find
A sweeter sound than Thy blest name,
O Savior of mankind!

3

O Hope of ev'ry contrite heart,
O Joy of all the meek!
To those who fall, how kind Thou art,
How good to those who seek!

4

But what to those who find? Ah! this
No tongue nor pen can show;
The love of Jesus, what it is,
None but His loved ones know.

5

Jesus, our only Joy be Thou
As Thou our Prize wilt be!
Jesus, be Thou our Glory now
And through eternity.

Jesus, Jesus, Only Jesus

Jesus, Jesus, nichts als Jesus—8. 7. 8. 7. 7. 7.

Ludaemilia Elisabeth, 1687
Tr., August Crull, 1880, alt.

"Vollkommenes Choralbuch,"
Hamburg, 1715

1 Je-sus, Je-sus, on-ly Je-sus, Can my heart-felt long-ing still.

Lo, I pledge my-self to Je-sus What He wills a-lone to will.

For my heart, which He hath filled, Ev-er cries, Lord, as Thou wilt.

2

One there is for whom I'm living,
　Whom I love most tenderly;
Unto Jesus I am giving
　What in love He gave to me.
Jesus' blood hides all my guilt;
Lord, oh, lead me as Thou wilt.

3

What to me may seem a treasure
　But displeasing is to Thee,
Oh, remove such harmful pleasure;
　Give instead what profits me.
Let my heart by Thee be stilled;
Make me Thine, Lord, as Thou wilt.

4

Let me earnestly endeavor
　Thy good pleasure to fulfill;
In me, through me, with me, ever,
　Lord, accomplish Thou Thy will.
In Thy holy image built,
Let me die, Lord, as Thou wilt.

5

Jesus, constant be my praises,
　For Thou unto me didst bring
Thine own self and all Thy graces
　That I joyfully may sing:
Be it unto me, my Shield,
As Thou wilt, Lord, as Thou wilt.

130

Jesus Sinners Doth Receive

Meinen Jesum lass' ich nicht—7, 8. 7. 8. 7. 7.

Erdmann Neumeister, 1718, cento
Tr., composite

"Neuverfertigtes Gesangbuch"
Darmstadt, 1699

1 Je-sus sin-ners doth re-ceive; Oh, may all this say-ing pon-der Who in sin's de-lu-sions live And from God and heav-en wan-der! Here is hope for all who grieve- Je-sus sin-ners doth re-ceive.

2

We deserve but grief and shame,
Yet His words, rich grace revealing,
Pardon, peace, and life proclaim.
Here their ills have perfect healing
Who with humble hearts believe—
Jesus sinners doth receive.

3

Sheep that from the fold did stray
No true shepherd e'er forsaketh;
Weary souls that lost their way
Christ, the Shepherd, gently taketh
In His arms that they may live—
Jesus sinners doth receive.

4

Come, ye sinners, one and all,
Come, accept His invitation;
Come, obey His gracious call,
Come and take His free salvation!
Firmly in these words believe:
Jesus sinners doth receive.

5

Jesus sinners doth receive.
Also I have been forgiven;
And when I this earth must leave,
I shall find an open heaven.
Dying, still to Him I cleave—
Jesus sinners doth receive.

See also:

Jesus, King of Glory
There Is a Name I Love to Hear
Thee Will I Love, My Strength, My Tower

God Loved the World So that He Gave
Beautiful Savior
Sun of My Soul, Thou Savior Dear

My Heart is Longing to Praise My Savior

Princess Eugenie—10. 10. 10. 10.

Princess Eugenie of Sweden
Tr., P. A. Sveeggen, 1931

Norwegian folk tune

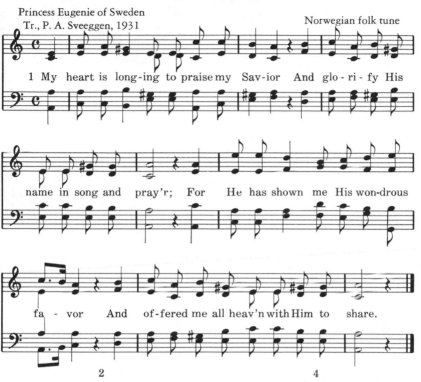

1 My heart is long-ing to praise my Sav-ior And glo-ri-fy His name in song and pray'r; For He has shown me His won-drous fa - vor And of-fered me all heav'n with Him to share.

2

O blessed Jesus, what Thou hast given
Through dying on the cross in
bitter pain
Has filled my heart with the peace
of heaven;
My winter's gone, and spring is
mine again.

3

O Christian friends, let our song,
ascending,
Give honor, praise to Him who set
us free!
Our tribulations may seem unending,
But soon with Him we shall forever be.

4

To Thee, O Savior, our adoration
Shall rise forever for Thy precious
blood,
Which blotted out all the accusation
Of sin and guilt which once against
us stood.

5

What blessed joy overflows my spirit,
Because Thy wondrous grace was
granted me.
Thy work complete, that I may
inherit
At last eternal life in heaven with
Thee!

132

I Am Trusting Thee, Lord Jesus

Stephanos—8. 5. 8. 3.

Frances R. Havergal, 1874   Henry W. Baker, 1868

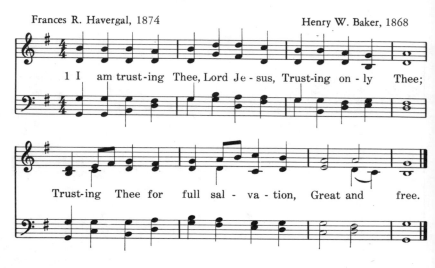

1 I am trust-ing Thee, Lord Je-sus, Trust-ing on-ly Thee;

Trust-ing Thee for full sal-va-tion, Great and free.

2
I am trusting Thee for pardon;
  At Thy feet I bow,
For Thy grace and tender mercy
  Trusting now.

3
I am trusting Thee for cleansing
  In the crimson flood;
Trusting Thee to make me holy
  By Thy blood.

4
I am trusting Thee to guide me;
  Thou alone shalt lead,
Ev'ry day and hour supplying
  All my need.

5
I am trusting Thee for power;
  Thine can never fail.
Words which Thou Thyself shalt give
  me
    Must prevail.

6
I am trusting Thee, Lord Jesus;
  Never let me fall.
I am trusting Thee forever
  And for all.

Jesus, Savior, Pilot Me

Pilot—7. 7. 7. 7. 7. 7.

Edward Hopper, 1871   John E. Gould, 1871

1 Je - sus, Sav - ior, pi - lot me O - ver life's tem - pes-tuous sea, Un - known waves be - fore me roll, Hid - ing rock and treach-'rous shoal. Chart and com - pass come from Thee; Je - sus, Sav - ior, pi - lot me.

2

As a mother stills her child,
Thou canst hush the ocean wild;
Boist'rous waves obey Thy will
When Thou say'st to them, "Be still!"
Wondrous Sov'reign of the sea,
Jesus, Savior, pilot me.

3

When at last I near the shore
And the fearful breakers roar
'Twixt me and the peaceful rest,
Then, while leaning on Thy breast,
May I hear Thee say to me,
"Fear not, I will pilot thee."

134

The Lord's My Shepherd, I'll Not Want

Belmont—C. M.

Francis Rous, et al., 1650   William Gardiner, 1812

1 The Lord's my Shep-herd, I'll not want; He makes me down to lie In pas-tures green; He lead-eth me The qui-et wa-ters by.

2

My soul He doth restore again
   And me to walk doth make
Within the paths of righteousness,
   E'en for His own name's sake.

3

Yea, though I walk in death's dark
    vale,
   Yet will I fear no ill;
For Thou art with me, and Thy rod
   And staff me comfort still.

4

My table Thou hast furnished
   In presence of my foes;
My head Thou dost with oil anoint,
   And my cup overflows.

5

Goodness and mercy, all my life,
   Shall surely follow me;
And in God's house forevermore
   My dwelling place shall be.

Chief of Sinners Though I Be

Gethsemane—7. 7. 7. 7. 7. 7.

William McComb, 1864

Richard Redhead, 1853

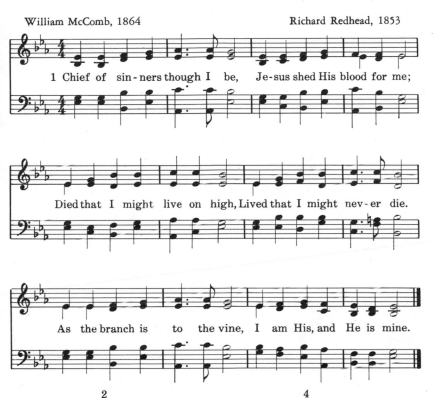

1 Chief of sin-ners though I be, Je-sus shed His blood for me;

Died that I might live on high, Lived that I might nev-er die.

As the branch is to the vine, I am His, and He is mine.

2

Oh, the height of Jesus' love!
Higher than the heav'ns above,
Deeper than the depths of sea,
Lasting as eternity.
Love that found me—wondrous
        thought!
Found me when I sought Him not.

3

Jesus only can impart
Balm to heal the smitten heart;
Peace that flows from sin forgiv'n,
Joy that lifts the soul to heav'n;
Faith and hope to walk with God
In the way that Enoch trod.

4

Chief of sinners though I be,
Christ is All in all to me;
All my wants to Him are known,
All my sorrows are His own.
Safe with Him from earthly strife,
He sustains the hidden life.

5

O my Savior, help afford
By Thy Spirit and Thy Word!
When my wayward heart would stray,
Keep me in the narrow way;
Grace in time of need supply
While I live and when I die.

Jesus, Thy Blood and Righteousness

St. Crispin—L.M.

Ludwig von Zinzendorf, 1739, cento
Tr., John Wesley, 1740
George J. Elvey, 1862

1 Je-sus, Thy blood and right-eous-ness My beau-ty are, my glo-rious dress; Midst flam-ing worlds, in these ar-rayed, With joy shall I lift up my head.

2
Bold shall I stand in that great Day,
For who aught to my charge shall
    lay?
Fully through these absolved I am
From sin and fear, from guilt and
    shame.

3
The holy, meek, unspotted Lamb,
Who from the Father's bosom came,
Who died for me, e'en me t' atone,
Now for my Lord and God I own.

4
Lord, I believe Thy precious blood
Which at the mercy seat of God
Forever doth for sinners plead,
For me—e'en for my soul—was shed.

5
Lord, I believe were sinners more
Than sands upon the ocean shore,
Thou hast for all a ransom paid,
For all a full atonement made.

6
When from the dust of death I rise
To claim my mansion in the skies,
E'en then this shall be all my plea:
Jesus hath lived and died for me.

7
Jesus, be endless praise to Thee,
Whose boundless mercy hath for me,
For me, and all Thy hands have made,
An everlasting ransom paid.

Rock of Ages, Cleft for Me

Toplady—7. 7. 7. 7. 7. 7.

Augustus M. Toplady, 1776, alt.   Thomas Hastings, 1830

1 Rock of A - ges, cleft for me, Let me hide my-self in Thee;

Let the wa - ter and the blood From Thy riv - en side which flowed

Be of sin the dou - ble cure, Cleanse me from its guilt and pow'r.

2
Not the labors of my hands
Can fulfill Thy Law's demands;
Could my zeal no respite know,
Could my tears forever flow,
All for sin could not atone;
Thou must save, and Thou alone.

3
Nothing in my hand I bring,
Simply to Thy Cross I cling;
Naked, come to Thee for dress;
Helpless, look to Thee for grace;
Foul, I to the fountain fly—
Wash me, Savior, or I die!

4
While I draw this fleeting breath,
When mine eyelids close in death,.
When I soar to worlds unknown,
See Thee on Thy judgment throne,
Rock of Ages, cleft for me,
Let me hide myself in Thee!

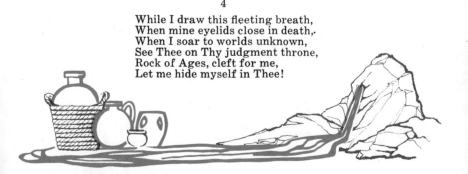

The King of Love My Shepherd Is

First Tune—St. Columba—8. 7. 8. 7., Iambic

Henry W. Baker, 1868   Ancient Irish hymn melody

1 The King of Love my Shep - herd is, Whose good - ness fail - eth nev - er; I noth - ing lack if I am His And He is mine for - ev - er.

2

Where streams of living water flow,
  My ransomed soul He leadeth,
And where the verdant pastures grow,
  With food celestial feedeth.

3

Perverse and foolish, oft I strayed,
  But yet in love He sought me
And on His shoulder gently laid
  And home, rejoicing, brought me.

4

In death's dark vale I fear no ill
  With Thee, dear Lord, beside me;
Thy rod and staff my comfort still,
  Thy cross before to guide me.

5

Thou spreadst a table in my sight,
  Thy unction grace bestoweth;
And, oh! the transport of delight
  With which my cup o'erfloweth!

6

And so through all the length of days
  Thy goodness faileth never.
Good Shepherd, may I sing Thy praise
  Within Thy house forever!

The King of Love My Shepherd Is

Second Tune—Ich dank' dir schon—8. 7. 8. 7., Iambic

Henry W. Baker, 1868
Michael Praetorius, 1610

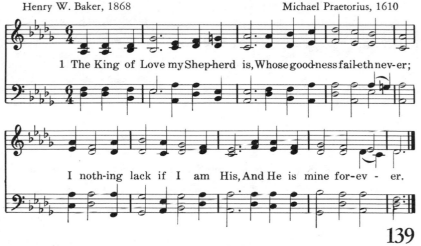

1 The King of Love my Shep-herd is, Whose good-ness fail-eth nev-er;

I noth-ing lack if I am His, And He is mine for-ev - er.

139

He Cares for Me

Palestrina—8. 8. 8. 4.

Author unknown
Giovanni P. da Palestrina, 1591, ad.

1 How strong and sweet my Fa-ther's care, That round a - bout me,

like the air, Is with me al-ways, ev - 'ry-where! He cares for me.

2
The thought great wonder with it
    brings;
My cares are all such little things;
But to the truth my glad heart clings:
    He cares for me.

3
Oh, keep me ever in Thy love,
Dear Father, watching from above;
And as through life my steps shall
    move,
    Oh, care for me.

My Hope Is Built on Nothing Less

Magdalen—8. 8. 8. 8. 8. 8.

Edward Mote, c. 1834, cento

John Stainer, 1873, arr.

1 My hope is built on noth-ing less Than Je - sus' blood and right-eous-ness; I dare not trust the sweet-est frame, But whol - ly lean on Je - sus' name. On Christ, the sol - id Rock, I stand; All oth - er ground is sink - ing sand.

2

When darkness veils His lovely face,
I rest on His unchanging grace;
In ev'ry high and stormy gale
My anchor holds within the veil.
On Christ, the solid Rock, I stand;
All other ground is sinking sand.

3

His oath, His covenant, and blood
Support me in the whelming flood;
When ev'ry earthly prop gives way,
He then is all my Hope and Stay.
On Christ, the solid Rock, I stand;
All other ground is sinking sand.

4

When He shall come with trumpet
    sound,
Oh, may I then in Him be found,
Clothed in His righteousness alone,
Faultless to stand before the throne.
On Christ, the solid Rock, I stand;
All other ground is sinking sand.

141

Faithful Shepherd, Feed Me

Sandown—6. 5. 6. 5.

Author unknown

J. F. Swift

1 Faith-ful Shep-herd, feed me In the pas-tures green;

Faith.-ful Shep-herd, lead me Where Thy steps are seen.

2

Hold me fast, and guide me
    In the narrow way,
So, with Thee beside me,
    I shall never stray.

3

Daily bring me nearer
    To the heavenly shore;
May my faith grow clearer,
    May I love Thee more.

4

Hallow every pleasure,
    Every gift and pain;
Be Thyself my Treasure,
    Though none else I gain.

5

Give me joy or sadness;
    This be all my care,
That eternal gladness
    I with Thee may share.

6

Day by day prepare me
As Thou seest best,
Then let angels bear me
To Thy promised rest.

Thy Way, Not Mine, O Lord

Ich halte treulich still—6. 6. 6. 6. D.

Horatius Bonar, 1857, cento

"Musikalisches Gesangbuch"
Leipzig, 1736, ad.

1 Thy way, not mine, O Lord, How-ev-er dark it be.

Lead me by Thine own hand; Choose Thou the path for me.

I dare not choose my lot; I would not if I might.

Choose Thou for me, my God; So shall I walk a-right.

2
Choose Thou for me my friends,
My sickness or my health;
Choose Thou my cares for me,
My poverty or wealth.
Not mine,not mine, the choice
In things or great or small;
Be Thou my Guide, my Strength,
My Wisdom, and my All.

My Faith Looks Up to Thee

Olivet—6. 6. 4. 6. 6. 6. 4.

Ray Palmer, 1830

Lowell Mason, 1831

1 My faith looks up to Thee, Thou Lamb of Cal - va - ry, Sav - ior di - vine. Now hear me while I pray; Take all my guilt a - way; Oh, let me from this day Be whol - ly Thine!

2
May Thy rich grace impart
Strength to my fainting heart,
   My zeal inspire!
As Thou hast died for me,
Oh, may my love to Thee
Pure, warm, and changeless be,
   A living fire!

3
While life's dark maze I tread
And griefs around me spread,
   Be Thou my Guide.
Bid darkness turn to day,
Wipe sorrow's tears away,
Nor let me ever stray
   From Thee aside.

4
When ends life's transient dream,
When death's cold, sullen stream
   Shall o'er me roll,
Blest Savior, then, in love,
Fear and distrust remove;
Oh, bear me safe above,
   A ransomed soul!

See also:
A Mighty Fortress Is Our God
Guide Me, O Thou Great Jehovah

All Depends on Our Possessing
Lord, I Confess Thy Tender Care

144

Praise God, from Whom All Blessings Flow

Old Hundredth—L. M.

Thomas Ken, 1695   "Genevan Psalter," 1551

Praise God, from whom all bless - ings flow; Praise
Him, all crea-tures here be - low; Praise Him a - bove, ye
heav'n - ly host: Praise Fa - ther, Son, and Ho - ly Ghost.

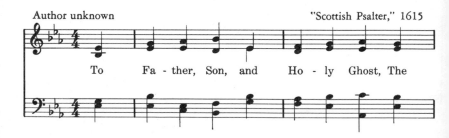

145

To Father, Son, and Holy Ghost

Dundee—C. M.

Author unknown   "Scottish Psalter," 1615

To Fa - ther, Son, and Ho - ly Ghost, The

God whom we a - dore, Be glo - ry, as it
was, is now, And shall be ev - er - more.

146

God the Father, Bless Us

St. Martin—6. 6. 6. 7.

Author unknown   Caspar Ett, "Cantica Sacra," 1840

God the Fa - ther, bless us; God the Son, de - fend us;

God the Spir - it, keep us, Now and ev - er - more. A-men.

147

Bless, O Lord, the Off'rings

Offering—6. 5. 6. 5.

Author unknown

Composer unknown

1 Bless, O Lord, the of-f'rings Which thy chil-dren lay

At Thy feet, re - joic - ing On this ho - ly day.

2
With Thy death Thou gavest
Wealth of love untold;
In Thy loving service
Let us ne'er grow cold.

148

We Give Thee But Thine Own

Energy—S. M.

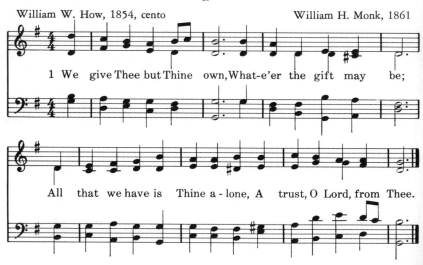

William W. How, 1854, cento

William H. Monk, 1861

1 We give Thee but Thine own, What-e'er the gift may be;

All that we have is Thine a - lone, A trust, O Lord, from Thee.

2
May we Thy bounties thus
  As stewards true receive
And gladly, as Thou blessest us,
  To Thee our first fruits give!

3
The captive to release,
  To God the lost to bring,
To teach the way of life and peace,
  It is a Christlike thing.

4
And we believe Thy Word,
  Though dim our faith may be:
Whate'er for Thine we do, O Lord,
  We do it unto Thee.

149

All Things Are Thine

Germany—L. M.

Sacred Melodies, 1815
Arr. by William Gardiner

John Greenleaf Whittier, 1807-1892

1 All things are Thine; no gift have we, Lord of all gifts, to of - fer Thee; And hence with grate - ful hearts to - day Thine own be - fore Thy feet we lay.

See also:
We Praise Thee, O God, Our Redeemer, Creator
Praise to the Lord, the Almighty

Now Thank We All Our God
Take My Life and Let It Be

The WORD

150

Holy Bible, Book Divine

Posen—7. 7. 7. 7.

John Burton, alt.   Georg Christoph Strattner, 1691

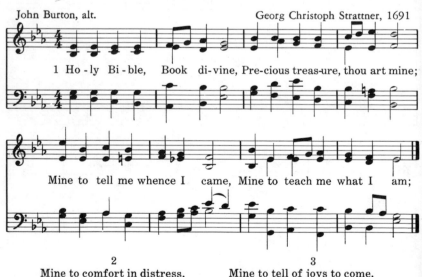

1 Ho-ly Bi-ble, Book di-vine, Pre-cious treas-ure, thou art mine;
Mine to tell me whence I came, Mine to teach me what I am;

2
Mine to comfort in distress,
If the Holy Spirit bless;
Mine to show by living faith
Man can triumph over death;

3
Mine to tell of joys to come,
Light and life beyond the tomb.
Holy Bible, Book divine,
Precious treasure, thou art mine.

Father of Mercies, in Thy Word

Bedford—C. M.

Anne Steele, 1760, cento

William Wheall, 1729

1 Fa - ther of mer - cies, in Thy Word What end - less glo - ry shines! For - ev - er be Thy name a - dored For these ce - les - tial lines!

2
Here may the blind and hungry come
  And light and food receive;
Here shall the lowliest guest have
    room
  And taste and see and live.

3
Here springs of consolation rise
  To cheer the fainting mind,
And thirsting souls receive supplies
  And sweet refreshment find.

4
Here the Redeemer's welcome voice
  Spreads heav'nly peace around,
And life and everlasting joys
  Attend the blissful sound.

5
Oh, may these heavenly pages be
  My ever dear delight;
And still new beauties may I see
  And still increasing light!

6
Divine Instructor, gracious Lord,
  Be Thou forever near;
Teach me to love Thy sacred Word
  And view my Savior here.

152

Thy Word Is Like a Garden, Lord

Bethlehem—C. M. D.

Edwin Hodder, 1837-1904

Gottfried W. Fink, 1842

1 Thy Word is like a gar-den, Lord, With flow-ers bright and fair;

And ev-'ry one who seeks may pluck A love-ly clus-ter there.

Thy Word is like a deep, deep mine, And jew-els rich and rare

Are hid-den in its might-y depths For ev-'ry search-er there.

2
Thy Word is like a starry host:
A thousand rays of light
Are seen to guide the traveler
And make his pathway bright.
Thy Word is like an armory
Where soldiers may repair
And find for life's long battle day
All needful weapons there.

3
Oh, may I love Thy precious Word,
May I explore the mine,
May I its fragrant flowers glean,
May light upon me shine!
Oh, may I find my armor there,
Thy Word my trusty sword!
I'll learn to fight with ev'ry foe
The battle of the Lord.

Great God, with Wonder and with Praise

Dundee—C. M.

Author unknown   "Scottish Psalter," 1615

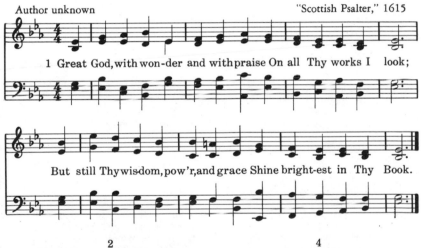

1 Great God, with won-der and with praise On all Thy works I look;

But still Thy wisdom, pow'r, and grace Shine bright-est in Thy Book.

2

Here are my choicest treasures hid,
 Here my best comfort lies,
Here my desires are satisfied,
 And here my hopes arise.

3

Lord, may I understand Thy Law;
 Show what my faults have been,
And from Thy Gospel let me draw
 Pardon for all my sin.

4

Here would I learn how Christ has
  died
 To save my soul from hell;
Not all the books on earth beside
 Such heav'nly wonders tell.

5

Then let me love my Bible more
 And take a fresh delight
By day to read these wonders o'er
 And meditate by night.

154

My Bible! 'Tis a Book Divine

Angelus—L. M.

Author unknown

"Heilige Seelenlust"
Breslau, 1657, ad.

1 My Bi - ble! 'Tis a Book di - vine, Where heav'n - ly truth and mer - cy shine, And wis-dom speaks in ev - 'ry line, And speaks to me, And speaks to me.

2
My Bible! In this Book alone
I find God's holy will made known;
And here His love to man is shown,
His love to me, His love to me.

3
My Bible! Here with joy I trace
The records of redeeming grace;
Glad tidings to a sinful race,
Good news to me, Good news to me.

4
My Bible! Here it is I read
How Jesus did for sinners bleed.
Oh. this was wondrous love indeed:
Christ bled for me, Christ bled for me!

5
My Bible! Oh, that I may ne'er
Consult it but with faith and prayer
That I may see my Savior there,
Who died for me, Who died for me.

How Precious Is the Book Divine

Walder—C. M.

John Fawcett, 1782

Johann J. Walder, 1788

1 How precious is the Book Divine, By inspiration giv'n! Bright as a lamp its doctrines shine To guide our souls to heav'n.

2
Its light, descending from above
Our gloomy world to cheer,
Displays a Savior's boundless love
And brings His glories near.

3
It shows to man his wand'ring ways
And where his feet have trod,
And brings to view the matchless
grace
Of a forgiving God.

4
O'er all the straight and narrow way
Its radiant beams are cast;
A light whose never weary ray
Grows brightest at the last.

5
It sweetly cheers our drooping hearts
In this dark vale of tears.
Life, light, and joy it still imparts
And quells our rising fears.

6
This lamp through all the tedious
night
Of life shall guide our way,
Till we behold the clearer light
Of an eternal day.

156

O God of Light, Thy Word, a Lamp Unfailing

Charterhouse—11. 10. 11. 10.

Sarah E. Taylor, 1952

David Evans, 1927

1 O God of Light, Thy Word, a Lamp un-fail-ing,
Shines through the dark-ness of our earth-ly way,
O'er fear and doubt, o'er black de-spair pre-vail-ing,
Guid-ing our steps to Thine e-ter-nal day.

2
From days of old, through swiftly
rolling ages,
Thou hast revealed Thy will to
mortal men,
Speaking to saints, to prophets,
kings, and sages,
Who wrote the message with immortal pen.

3
Undimmed by time, the Word is still
revealing
To sinful men Thy justice and Thy
grace;
And questing hearts that long for
peace and healing
See Thy compassion in the Savior's face.

4

To all the world the message Thou
  art sending,
To ev'ry land, to ev'ry race and
  clan;
And myriad tongues, in one great
  anthem blending,
Acclaim with joy Thy wondrous
  gift to man.

157

Almighty God, Thy Word Is Cast

Dundee—C. M.

John Cawood, 1819   "Scottish Psalter," 1615

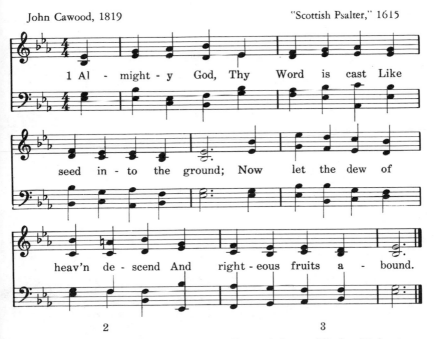

1 Al - might - y God, Thy Word is cast Like
seed in - to the ground; Now let the dew of
heav'n de - scend And right - eous fruits a - bound.

2

Let not the foe of Christ and man
  This holy seed remove,
But give it root in ev'ry heart
  To bring forth fruits of love.

3

Let not the world's deceitful cares
  The rising plant destroy,
But let it yield a hundredfold
  The fruits of peace and joy.

4

Oft as the precious seed is sown,
  Thy quickening grace bestow
That all whose souls the truth receive
  Its saving power may know.

O Word of God Incarnate

Munich—7 6. 7. 6. D.

William W. How, 1867

"Neuvermehrtes Gesangbuch"
Meiningen, 1693

1 O Word of God In-car-nate, O Wis-dom from on high,

O Truth un-changed, un-chang-ing, O Light of our dark sky—

We praise Thee for the ra-diance That from the hal-lowed page,

A lan-tern to our foot-steps, Shines on from age to age.

2
The Church from her dear Master
  Received the gift divine,
And still that light she lifteth
  O'er all the earth to shine.
It is the golden casket
  Where gems of truth are stored;
It is the heav'n-drawn picture
  Of Christ, the living Word.

3
Oh, make Thy Church, dear Savior,
  A lamp of burnished gold
To bear before the nations
  Thy true light as of old!
Oh, teach Thy wand'ring pilgrims
  By this their path to trace
Till, clouds and darkness ended,
  They see Thee face to face!

159

Oh, that the Lord Would Guide My Ways

Evan—C. M.

Isaac Watts, 1719, cento, alt.   William H. Havergal, 1846

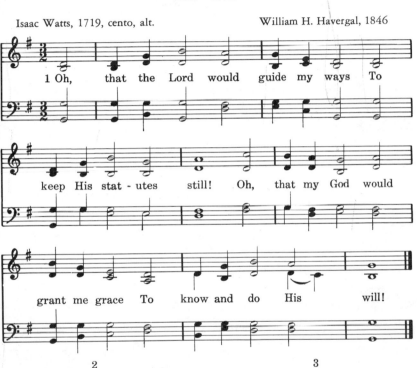

1 Oh, that the Lord would guide my ways To keep His stat-utes still! Oh, that my God would grant me grace To know and do His will!

2
Order my footsteps by Thy Word,
And make my heart sincere;
Let sin have no dominion, Lord,
But keep my conscience clear.

3
Assist my soul, too apt to stray,
A stricter watch to keep;
And should I e'er forget Thy way,
Restore Thy wand'ring sheep.

4
Make me to walk in Thy commands —
'Tis a delightful road —
Nor let my head or heart or hands
Offend against my God.

Lord, Thy Word, That Sacred Treasure

O du Liebe—8. 7. 8. 7. D.

Count Ludwig von Zinzendorf, 1725   "Musikalischer Christenschatz"
Tr., H. Brueckner, 1925   Basel, 1745

1. Lord, Thy Word, that sa-cred Treas-ure Let me ev-er-more re-tain; Naught on earth can give the pleas-ure That I from its wealth may gain. Were Thy truth no more to guide us, How our faith would go a-stray! Lord, what-ev-er may be-tide us, Let this Light il-lume our way.

2

Hallelujah, now and ever
  Be Thy truth my stay, O Lord!
Grant in mercy that I never
  Cease to love Thy precious Word.
By its teachings, so appealing,
  May it keep me firm and true;
At Thy feet, with Mary kneeling,
  I would learn Thy will to do.

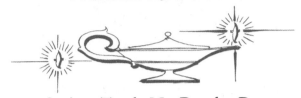

161

Savior, Teach Me Day by Day

Hoechster Priester—7. 7. 7. 7.

"Musikalischer Christenschatz"
Basel, 1745

Jane E. Leeson, 1807-1882

1 Sav-ior, teach me day by day Love's sweet les-son to o-bey;

Sweet-er les-son can-not be, Lov-ing Him who first loved me.

2

With a childlike heart of love
At Thy bidding may I move;
Prompt to serve and follow Thee,
Loving Him who first loved me.

3

Teach me all Thy steps to trace,
Strong to follow in Thy grace;
Learning how to love from Thee,
Loving Him who first loved me.

4

Love in loving finds employ,
In obedience all her joy;
Ever new that joy will be,
Loving Him who first loved me.

5

Thus may I rejoice to show
That I feel the love I owe;
Singing, till Thy face I see,
Of His love who first loved me.

162

I Pray Thee, Dear Lord Jesus

Jeg vil mig Herren love—7. 6. 7. 6. D.

Thomas Kingo, 1699
Tr., Norman A. Madson, 1939

Hartnack Zinck's "Koralbog," 1801

1 I pray Thee, dear Lord Je - sus, My heart to keep and train

That I Thy ho - ly tem - ple From youth to age re - main.

Turn Thou my thoughts for - ev - er From world-ly wis-dom's lore;

If I but learn to know Thee, I shall not want for more.

How Shall the Young Secure Their Hearts

St. Peter—C. M.

Isaac Watts, 1719, cento

Alexander R. Reinagle, 1830

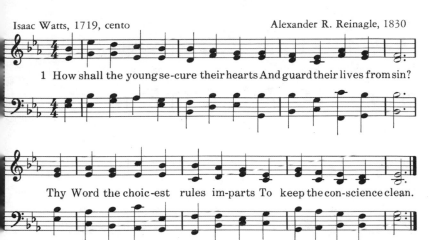

1 How shall the young se-cure their hearts And guard their lives from sin?

Thy Word the choic-est rules im-parts To keep the con-science clean.

2
'Tis, like the sun, a heav'nly light
   That guides us all the day,
And through the dangers of the night
   A lamp to lead our way.

3
The starry heav'ns Thy rule obey,
   The earth maintains her place;
And these Thy servants, night and
      day,
   Thy skill and pow'r express.

4
But still Thy Law and Gospel, Lord,
   Have lessons more divine;
Not earth stands firmer than Thy
      Word,
   Nor stars so nobly shine.

5
Thy Word is everlasting truth;
   How pure is every page!
That holy Book shall guide our youth
   And well support our age.

164

The Gospel Shows the Father's Grace

Herr Jesu Christ, dich—L. M.

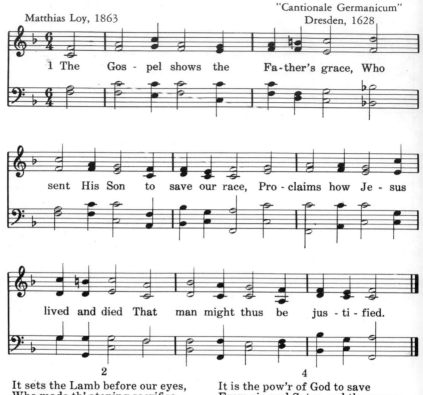

Matthias Loy, 1863

"Cantionale Germanicum"
Dresden, 1628

1 The Gos - pel shows the Fa - ther's grace, Who sent His Son to save our race, Pro - claims how Je - sus lived and died That man might thus be jus - ti - fied.

2

It sets the Lamb before our eyes,
Who made th' atoning sacrifice,
And calls the souls with guilt opprest
To come and find eternal rest.

3

It brings the Savior's righteousness
Our souls to robe in royal dress;
From all our guilt it brings release
And gives the troubled conscience
peace.

4

It is the pow'r of God to save
From sin and Satan and the grave;
It works the faith, which firmly clings
To all the treasures which it brings.

5

It bears to all the tidings glad
And bids their hearts no more be
sad;
The heavy-laden souls it cheers
And banishes their guilty fears.

6

May we in faith its tidings learn
Nor thanklessly its blessings spurn;
May we in faith its truth confess
And praise the Lord our Righteous-
ness!

The Law of God Is Good and Wise

Erhalt uns, Herr—L. M.

"Geistliche Lieder"
Wittenberg, 1543

Matthias Loy, 1863, cento

1 The Law of God is good and wise And sets His will be-fore our eyes, Shows us the way of right-eous-ness, And dooms to death when we trans-gress.

2
To those who help in Christ have
found
And would in works of love abound
It shows what deeds are His delight
And should be done as good and right.

3
The Law is good; but since the Fall
Its holiness condemns us all;
It dooms us for our sin to die
And has no power to justify.

4
To Jesus we for refuge flee,
Who from the curse has set us free,
And humbly worship at His throne,
Saved by His grace through faith
alone.

See also:
Lord, Keep Us Steadfast in Thy Word
Faithful Shepherd, Feed Me

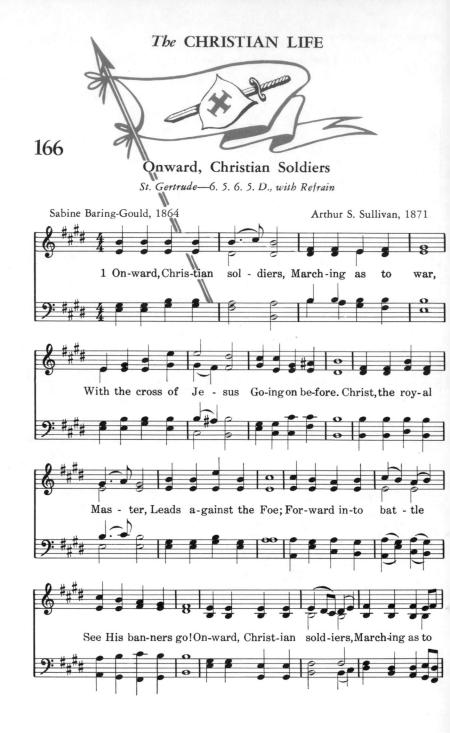

166

Onward, Christian Soldiers

St. Gertrude—6. 5. 6. 5. D., with Refrain

Sabine Baring-Gould, 1864

Arthur S. Sullivan, 1871

1 On-ward, Chris-tian sol - diers, March-ing as to war, With the cross of Je - sus Go-ing on be-fore. Christ, the roy-al Mas - ter, Leads a-gainst the Foe; For-ward in-to bat - tle See His ban-ners go! On-ward, Christ-ian sold-iers, March-ing as to

war, With the cross of Je-sus Go-ing on be-fore.

2

Like a mighty army
  Moves the Church of God;
Brothers, we are treading
  Where the saints have trod.
We are not divided,
  All one body we,
One in hope and doctrine,
  One in charity.
Onward, Christian soldiers,
  Marching as to war,
With the cross of Jesus
  Going on before.

3

Crowns and thrones may perish,
  Kingdoms rise and wane,
But the Church of Jesus
  Constant will remain.
Gates of hell can never
  'Gainst that Church prevail;
We have Christ's own promise,
  And that cannot fail.
Onward, Christian soldiers,
  Marching as to war,
With the cross of Jesus
  Going on before.

4

Onward, then, ye faithful,
  Join our happy throng,
Blend with ours your voices
  In the triumph song:
Glory, laud, and honor
  Unto Christ, the King;
This through countless ages
  Men and angels sing.
Onward, Christian soldiers,
  Marching as to war,
With the cross of Jesus
  Going on before.

Who Is on the Lord's Side?

Armageddon—6. 5. 6. 5., 12l.

Frances Ridley Havergal, 1836-1879

John Goss, 1800-1880

1 Who is on the Lord's side? Who will serve the King?
Who will be His help-ers Oth-er lives to bring? Who will leave the
world's side? Who will face the foe? Who is on the Lord's side?
Who for Him will go? By Thy call of mer-cy, By Thy
grace di-vine, We are on the Lord's side; Sav-ior, we are Thine.

2

Not for weight of glory,
  Not for crown and palm,
Enter we the army,
  Raise the warrior psalm;
But for Love that claimeth
  Lives for whom He died;
He whom Jesus nameth
  Must be on His side.
By Thy love constraining,
  By Thy grace divine,
We are on the Lord's side:
  Savior, we are Thine.

3

Fierce may be the conflict,
  Strong may be the foe,
But the King's own army
  None can overthrow.
Round His standard ranging,
  Vict'ry is secure;
For His Truth unchanging
  Makes the triumph sure.
Joyfully enlisting,
  By Thy grace divine,
We are on the Lord's side:
  Savior, we are Thine.

168

Am I a Soldier of the Cross
Winchester Old—C. M.

Isaac Watts, 1721, alt.

"Psalter"
Thomas Este, 1592

1 Am I a sol-dier of the Cross, A foll-'wer of the Lamb,

And shall I fear to own His cause Or blush to speak His name?

2

Must I be carried to the skies
  On flow'ry beds of ease
While others fought to win the prize
  And sailed through bloody seas?

3

Are there no foes for me to face?
  Must I not stem the flood?
Is this vile world a friend to grace
  To help me on to God?

4

Sure I must fight if I would reign;
  Increase my courage, Lord!
I'll bear the toil, endure the pain,
  Supported by Thy Word.

5

Thy saints in all this glorious war
  Shall conquer though they die;
They see the triumph from afar
  With faith's discerning eye.

6

When that illustrious Day shall rise
  And all Thine armies shine
In robes of victory through the skies,
  The glory shall be Thine.

169

Stand Up, Stand Up for Jesus

Webb—7. 6. 7. 6. D.

George Duffield, 1858, cento   George J. Webb, 1837

1 Stand up, stand up for Je-sus, Ye sol-diers of the Cross!

Lift high His roy-al ban-ner, It must not suf-fer loss.

From vic-t'ry un-to vic-t'ry His ar-my shall He lead

Till ev-'ry foe is van-quished And Christ is Lord in-deed.

2

Stand up, stand up for Jesus!
  The trumpet call obey;
Forth to the mighty conflict
  In this His glorious day!
Ye that are men, now serve Him
  Against unnumbered foes;
Let courage rise with danger
  And strength to strength oppose.

3

Stand up, stand up for Jesus!
  Stand in His strength alone;
The arm of flesh will fail you,
  Ye dare not trust your own.
Put on the Gospel armor,
  Each piece put on with prayer;
Where duty calls or danger,
  Be never wanting there.

4

Stand up, stand up for Jesus!
  The strife will not be long;
This day the noise of battle,
  The next, the victor's song.
To him that overcometh
  A crown of life shall be;
He with the King of Glory
  Shall reign eternally.

170

My Soul, Be on Thy Guard

Schumann—S. M.

"Cantica Laudis"
Boston, 1850

George Heath, 1781

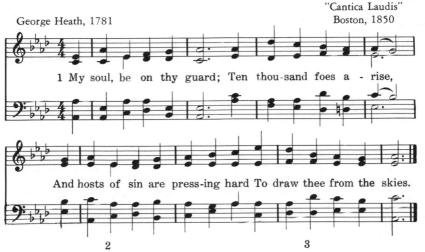

1 My soul, be on thy guard; Ten thou-sand foes a - rise,

And hosts of sin are press-ing hard To draw thee from the skies.

2

Oh, watch and fight and pray,
  The battle ne'er give o'er;
Renew it boldly ev'ry day,
  And help divine implore.

3

Ne'er think the victory won,
  Nor lay thine armor down;
Thine arduous work will not be done
  Till thou obtain thy crown.

4

Fight on, my soul, till death
  Shall bring thee to thy God;
He'll take thee at thy parting breath
  To His divine abode.

Fight the Good Fight with All Thy Might

Mendon—L. M.

John S. B. Monsell, 1863

German melody
Arr. by Samuel Dyer, 1828

1 Fight the good fight With all thy might; Christ is thy Strength and Christ thy Right. Lay hold on life, and it shall be Thy joy and crown e-ter-nal-ly.

2

Run the straight race Through God's good grace;
Lift up thine eyes and seek His face.
Life with its way before us lies;
Christ is the Path and Christ the Prize.

3

Cast care aside; Upon thy Guide
Lean, and His mercy will provide;
Lean, and the trusting soul shall prove
Christ is its Life and Christ its Love.

4

Faint not nor fear, His arms are near;
He changeth not, and thou art dear.
Only believe, and thou shalt see
That Christ is All in all to thee.

See also:

A Mighty Fortress Is Our God
Who Is on the Lord's Side?

Savior, While My Heart Is Tender

Ringe recht—8. 7. 8. 7.

Author unknown

"Musikalischer Christenschatz"
Basel, 1745

1 Sav - ior, while my heart is ten - der, I would
yield that heart to Thee; All my pow'rs to Thee sur -
ren - der, Thine, and on - ly Thine, to be.

2
Take me now, Lord Jesus, take me,
  Let my youthful heart be Thine;
Thy devoted servant make me,
  Fill my soul with love divine.

3
Let me do Thy will or bear it,
  I would know no will but Thine;
Should'st Thou take my life, or spare
    it,
  I that life to Thee resign.

4
Thine I am, O Lord, forever,
  To Thy service set apart;
Suffer me to leave Thee never;
  Seal Thine image on my heart.

173

O Jesus, I Have Promised

Munich—7. 6. 7. 6. D.

John E. Bode, 1816-1874

"Neuvermehrtes Gesangbuch"
Meiningen, 1693

1 O Je-sus, I have prom-ised To serve Thee to the end;

Be Thou for-ev-er near me, My Sav-ior and my Friend!

I shall not fear the bat-tle If Thou art by my side,

Nor wan-der from the path-way If Thou wilt be my Guide.

2
Oh, let me feel Thee near me,
  The world is ever near;
I see the sights that dazzle,
  The tempting sounds I hear.
My foes are ever near me,
  Around me and within;
But, Jesus, draw Thou nearer,
  And shield my soul from sin.

3
O Jesus, Thou hast promised
  To all who follow Thee
That where Thou art in glory
  There shall Thy servant be;
And, Jesus, I have promised
  To serve Thee to the end;
Oh, give me grace to follow,
  My Savior and my Friend.

Savior, I Follow On

Winterton—6. 4. 6. 4. 6. 6. 6. 4.

Charles S. Robinson, 1862

Joseph Barnby, 1892

1 Sav-ior, I fol-low on, Guid-ed by Thee,

See-ing not yet the hand That lead-eth me.

Hushed be my heart and still, Fear I no fur-ther ill,

On-ly to meet Thy will My will shall be.

2

Riven the rock for me
  Thirst to relieve,
Manna from heaven falls
  Fresh ev'ry eve.
Never a want severe
Causeth my eye a tear,
But Thou dost whisper near,
  "Only believe."

3

Savior, I long to walk
  Closer with Thee;
Led by Thy guiding hand,
  Ever to be
Constantly near Thy side,
Quickened and purified,
Living for Him who died
  Freely for me.

Thee Will I Love, My Strength, My Tower

Ich will dich lieben—9. 8. 9. 8. 8. 6.

Johann Scheffler, 1657, cento
Tr., Catherine Winkworth, 1863, alt.

"Harmonischer Liederschatz"
Frankfurt, 1738

1 Thee will I love, my Strength, my Tow-er; Thee will I love, my Hope, my Joy; Thee will I love with all my pow - er, With ar - dor time shall ne'er de-stroy. Thee will I love, O Light Di - vine, So long as life is mine.

2
Thee will I love, my Life, my Savior,
  Who art my best and truest Friend;
Thee will I love and praise forever,
  For never shall Thy kindness end;
Thee will I love with all my heart,
Thou my Redeemer art.

3
I thank Thee, Jesus, Sun from heaven,
  Whose radiance hath brought light
    to me;
I thank Thee, who hast richly given
  All that could make me glad and
    free;
I thank Thee that my soul is healed
By what Thy lips revealed.

4

Oh, teach me, Lord, to love Thee truly
With soul and body, head and heart,
And grant me grace that I may duly
Practice fore'er loves sacred art.
Grant that my every thought may be
Directed e'er to Thee.

5

Thee will I love, my Crown of gladness;
Thee will I love, my God and Lord,
Amid the darkest depths of sadness,
Nor for the hope of high reward—
For Thine own sake, O Light Divine,
So long as life is mine.

176

Take My Life and Let It Be

Patmos—7. 7. 7. 7,

Frances R. Havergal, 1874   William H. Havergal, 1869

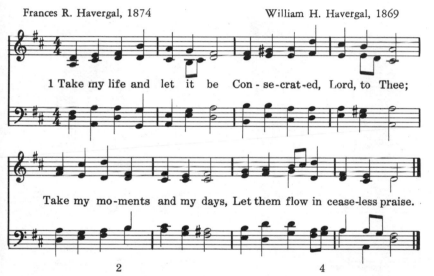

1 Take my life and let it be Con-se-crat-ed, Lord, to Thee;

Take my mo-ments and my days, Let them flow in cease-less praise.

2

Take my hands and let them move
At the impulse of Thy love;
Take my feet and let them be
Swift and beautiful for Thee.

4

Take my silver and my gold,
Not a mite would I withhold;
Take my intellect and use
Ev'ry pow'r as Thou shalt choose.

3

Take my voice and let me sing
Always, only, for my King;
Take my lips and let them be
Filled with messages from Thee.

5

Take my will and make it Thine,
It shall be no longer mine;
Take my heart, it is Thine own,
It shall be Thy royal throne.

6

Take my love, my Lord, I pour
At Thy feet its treasure store;
Take myself, and I will be
Ever, only, all, for Thee.

My Maker, Be Thou Nigh

Mein Schoepfer, steh mir bei— 6.6.6.6.7.7.7.7.8.6.

Johann J. Rambach, †1735
Tr., E. Taylor, 1925, alt.

Franz H. Meyer, 1740

1 My Mak-er, be Thou nigh The light of life to give,

And guide me with Thine eye While here on earth I live.

To Thee my heart I ten-der And all my pow'rs sur-ren-der;

Make it my one en-deav-or To love and serve Thee ev-er.

Up - on Thy prom-ise I re-ly; My Mak -er, be Thou nigh.

2

My Savior, wash me clean
 With Thy most precious blood,
That takes away all sin
 And seals my peace with God.
My soul in peace abideth
When in Thy wounds it hideth.
There I find full salvation
And freedom from damnation.
Without Thee lost, defiled by sin,
My Savior, wash me clean.

3

My Comforter, give pow'r
 That I may stand secure
When in temptation's hour
 The world and sin allure.
The Son to me revealing,
Inspire my thought and feeling,
His Word of grace to ponder,
Nor let me from Him wander.
On me Thy gifts and graces show'r:
My Comforter, give pow'r!

4

O Holy Trinity!
 To whom I all things owe,
Thine image graciously
 Within my heart bestow.
Choose me, though weak and lowly,
To be Thy temple holy
Where praise shall rise unending
For grace so condescending.
O heav'nly bliss, Thine own to be,
O Holy Trinity!

My Jesus, I Love Thee

Gordon—11. 11. 11. 11.

William R. Featherstone, 1842-1878
From The London Hymn Book, 1864   Adoniram J. Gordon, 1836-1895

1 My Jesus, I love Thee, I know Thou art mine,
For Thee all the follies of sin I resign;
My gracious Redeemer, my Savior art Thou;
If ever I loved Thee, Lord Jesus, 'tis now.

2
I love Thee, because Thou hast first
 loved me
And purchased my pardon on Calvary's tree;
I love Thee for wearing the thorns
 on Thy brow;
If ever I loved Thee, Lord Jesus,
 'tis now.

3
In mansions of glory and endless
 delight,
I'll ever adore Thee in heaven so
 bright;
I'll sing with the glittering crown on
 my brow;
If ever I loved Thee, Lord Jesus,
 'tis now.

All for Jesus

Consecration—8.7.8.7.

W. J. S. Simpson, 1887　　　　　　　　　　　　　John Stainer, 1887

1 All for Je - sus, all for Je - sus,
This our song shall ev - er be;
For we have no hope nor Sav - ior
If we have not hope in Thee.

2
All for Jesus—Thou wilt give us
　Strength to serve Thee hour by hour;
None can move us from Thy presence
　While we trust Thy love and pow'r.

3
All for Jesus—Thou hast loved us;
　All for Jesus—Thou hast died;
All for Jesus—Thou art with us;
　All for Jesus Crucified.

4
All for Jesus, all for Jesus,
　This the Church's song must be,
Till, at last, her sons are gathered
　One in love and one in Thee.

180

I Walk with Jesus All the Way

Der lieben Sonne Licht und Pracht—8. 7. 8. 7. 6. 6. 8. 8.

Hans A. Brorson, 1734
Tr., Ditlef G. Ristad, 1909, alt.

"Geistreiches Gesangbuch"
Halle, 1704

1 I walk with Je-sus all the way, His guid-ance nev-er fails me;
With-in His wounds I find a stay When Sa-tan's pow'r as-sails me;
And by His foot-steps led, My path I safe-ly tread.
In spite of ills that threat-en may, I walk with Je-sus all the way.

2

I walk with angels all the way,
 They shield me and befriend me;
All Satan's pow'r is held at bay
 When heav'nly hosts attend me;
They are my sure defense,
All fear and sorrow, hence!
Unharmed by foes, do what they may,
I walk with angels all the way.

3

My walk is heavenward all the way;
 Await, my soul, the morrow,
When thou shalt find release for aye
 From all thy sin and sorrow.
All worldly pomp, begone!
To heaven I now press on.
For all the world I would not stay;
My walk is heavenward all the way.

181

O God of Mercy, God of Might

Dunstan—8. 8. 8. 6.

Godfrey Thring, 1877   Joseph Barnby, 1883

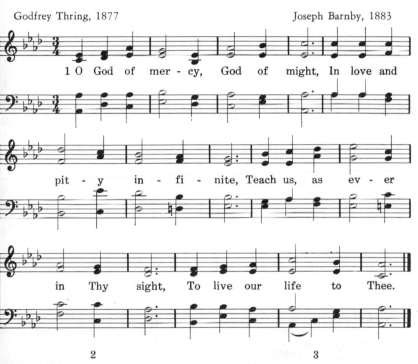

1 O God of mer - cy, God of might, In love and pit - y in - fi - nite, Teach us, as ev - er in Thy sight, To live our life to Thee.

2

And Thou, who cam'st on earth to die
That fallen men might live thereby,
Oh, hear us, for to Thee we cry,
In hope, O Lord, to Thee.

3

Teach us the lesson Thou hast taught,
To feel for those Thy blood hath
bought,
That ev'ry word and deed and thought
May work a work for Thee.

4

All are redeemed, both far and wide,
Since Thou, O Lord, for all hast died;
Then teach us, whatsoe'er betide,
To love them all in Thee.

Christ Is Kind and Gentle

Perrine—6. 5. 6. 5.

Cecil Frances Alexander, 1823-1895, alt.　　　　　　　Lee H. Bristol, Jr., 1953

1 Christ is kind and gen - tle, Christ is pure and true,

And His own dear chil - dren Must be ho - ly too.

2
There's a wicked spirit
　Watching round us still,
And he tries to tempt us
　To all harm and ill.

3
But we must not hear him
　Nor his bidding do,
But resist the evil
　And the good pursue.

4
For we promised truly
　In our infant days
To renounce him wholly
　And forsake his ways.

5
We are newborn Christians,
　We must learn to fight
With the bad within us
　And to do the right.

6
Christ is our own Savior,
　He is good and true,
And His own dear children
　Must be holy too.

Music from *Hymns for Children and Grownups.*　Copyright 1953 by Farrar, Straus
and Young.　Used by permission.

My God, Accept My Heart This Day

Winchester Old—C.M.

"Psalter"

Matthew Bridges, 1848   Thomas Este, 1592

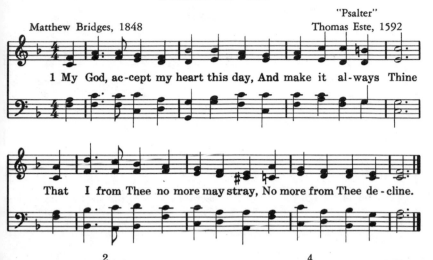

1 My God, ac-cept my heart this day, And make it al-ways Thine

That I from Thee no more may stray, No more from Thee de-cline.

2
Before the Cross of Him who died,
  Behold, I prostrate fall;
Let ev'ry sin be crucified
  And Christ be all in all.

3
Anoint me with Thy Spirit's grace,
  And seal me for Thine own,
That I may see Thy glorious face
  And worship near Thy throne.

4
May Thy dear blood once shed for me
  My blest atonement prove,
That I from first to last may be
  The purchase of Thy love!

5
Let every thought and work and word
  To Thee be ever given;
Then life shall be Thy service, Lord,
  And death the gate of heaven.

See also:

Jesus, Savior, Come to Me
I Pray Thee, Dear Lord Jesus
Jesus, I My Cross Have Taken

Let Me Be Thine Forever
Take Thou My Hands and Lead Me
Let Us Ever Walk with Jesus

Jesus, Lead Thou On

Seelenbraeutigam — 5. 5. 8. 8. 5. 5.

Ludwig von Zinzendorf, 1721
Cento by Christian Gregor, 1778
Tr., Jane Borthwick, 1854, alt.

Adam Drese, 1697

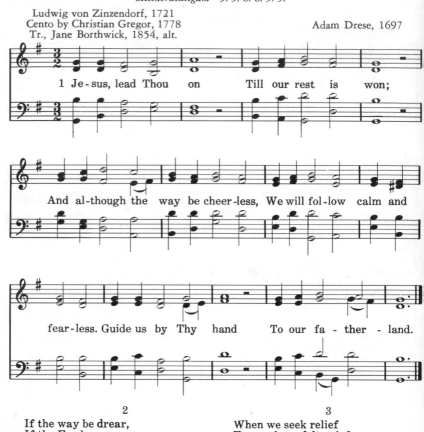

1 Je-sus, lead Thou on Till our rest is won; And al-though the way be cheer-less, We will fol-low calm and fear-less. Guide us by Thy hand To our fa - ther - land.

2
If the way be drear,
If the Foe be near,
Let not faithless fears o'ertake us;
Let not faith and hope forsake us;
For through many a woe
To our home we go.

3
When we seek relief
From a long-felt grief;
When temptations come alluring,
Make us patient and enduring;
Show us that bright shore
Where we weep no more.

4
Jesus, lead Thou on
Till our rest is won.
Heav'nly Leader, still direct us,
Still support, control, protect us,
Till we safely stand
In our fatherland.

185

Blessed Are the Sons of God

Voller Wunder—7. 7. 7. 7. 7. 7.

Joseph Humphreys, 1743, cento, alt. Johann G. Ebeling, 1666

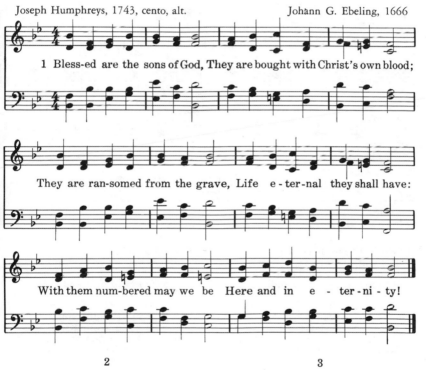

1 Bless-ed are the sons of God, They are bought with Christ's own blood;

They are ran-somed from the grave, Life e-ter-nal they shall have:

With them num-bered may we be Here and in e-ter-ni-ty!

2
They are justified by grace,
They enjoy the Savior's peace;
All their sins are washed away,
They shall stand in God's great Day:
With them numbered may we be
Here and in eternity!

3
They are lights upon the earth,
Children of a heav'nly birth;
One with God, with Jesus one;
Glory is in them begun:
With them numbered may we be
Here and in eternity!

I Love Thy Kingdom, Lord

St. Thomas—S. M.

Timothy Dwight, 1800, ab., alt.

Aaron Williams, 1770

1 I love Thy king-dom, Lord, The house of
Thine a - bode, The Church our blest Re - deem - er
saved With His own pre - cious blood.

2

I love Thy Church, O God.
  Her walls before Thee stand,
Dear as the apple of Thine eye
  And graven on Thy hand.

3

Should I with scoffers join
  Her altars to abuse?
No! Better far my tongue were dumb,
  My hand its skill should lose.

4

For her my tears shall fall,
  For her my prayers ascend,
To her my cares and toils be given
  Till toils and cares shall end.

5

Beyond my highest joy
  I prize her heavenly ways,
Her sweet communion, solemn vows,
  Her hymns of love and praise.

6

Jesus, Thou Friend Divine,
  Our Savior and our King,
Thy hand from every snare and foe
  Shall great deliverance bring.

7

Sure as Thy truth shall last,
  To Zion shall be given
The brightest glories earth can yield
  And brighter bliss of heaven.

For All Thy Saints, O Lord

Energy—S. M.

Richard Mant, 1837, cento

William H. Monk, 1861

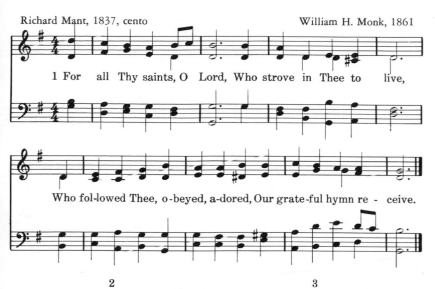

1 For all Thy saints, O Lord, Who strove in Thee to live,

Who fol-lowed Thee, o-beyed, a-dored, Our grate-ful hymn re - ceive.

2
For all Thy saints, O Lord,
Who strove in Thee to die,
Who counted Thee their great
Reward,
Accept our thankful cry.

3
They all in life and death,
With Thee, their Lord, in view,
Learned from Thy Holy Spirit's
breath
To suffer and to do.

4
For this Thy name we bless
And humbly pray that we
May follow them in holiness
And live and die in Thee.

Behold a Host, Arrayed in White

Great White Host—8. 8. 8. 6. 12 lines

Den store hvide Flok vi se
Hans A. Brorson, c. 1760
Tr., composite

Norwegian folk tune, c. 1600
Arr. by Edvard H. Grieg, †1907, ad.

1 Be - hold a host, ar - rayed in white, Like thou-sand snow-clad

moun-tains bright, With palms they stand. Who is this band Be-

fore the throne of light? Lo, these are they of

glo - rious fame Who from the great af - flic-tion came And

in the flood of Je - sus' blood Are cleansed from guilt and

blame. Now gath-ered in the ho - ly place, Their
voic - es they in wor-ship raise, Their an-thems swell where
God doth dwell, Mid an - gels' songs of praise.

2

Despised and scorned, they sojourned
   here;
But now, how glorious they appear!
Those martyrs stand, a priestly band,
God's throne forever near.
So oft, in troubled days gone by,
In anguish they would weep and sigh.
At home above the God of Love
For aye their tears shall dry.
They now enjoy their Sabbath rest,
The paschal banquet of the blest;
The Lamb, their Lord, at festal board
Himself is Host and Guest.

3

Then hail, ye mighty legions, yea,
All hail! Now safe and blest for aye,
And praise the Lord, who with His
   Word
Sustained you on the way.
Ye did the joys of earth disdain,
Ye toiled and sowed in tears and pain.
Farewell, now bring your sheaves
   and sing
Salvation's glad refrain.
Swing high your palms, lift up your
   song,
Yea, make it myriad voices strong.
Eternally shall praise to Thee,
God, and the Lamb belong.

The Church's One Foundation

Aurelia—7. 6. 7. 6. D.

Samuel J. Stone, 1866, cento   Samuel S. Wesley, 1864

1 The Church's one foun-da-tion Is Je-sus Christ, her Lord;
She is His new cre-a-tion By wa-ter and the Word.
From heav'n He came and sought her To be His ho-ly bride;
With His own blood He bought her, And for her life He died.

2
Elect from ev'ry nation,
  Yet one o'er all the earth,
Her charter of salvation
  One Lord, one faith, one birth.
One holy name she blesses,
  Partakes one holy food,
And to one hope she presses,
  With ev'ry grace endued.

3
The Church shall never perish!
  Her dear Lord, to defend,
To guide, sustain, and cherish,
  Is with her to the end.
Though there be those that hate her,
  False sons within her pale,
Against both foe and traitor
  She ever shall prevail.

Let the Song Go Round the Earth

Langdale—7. 5. 7. 5. 7. 7.

Sarah G. Stock, 1898

A. Somervell, 1863-1937

1 Let the song go round the earth, Je - sus Christ is Lord!

Sound His prais-es, tell His worth, Be His name a - dored!

Ev - 'ry clime and ev - 'ry tongue Join the grand, the glo-rious song!

2

Let the song go round the earth
  From the eastern sea,
Where the daylight has its birth,
  Glad and bright and free!
China's millions join the strains,
Send them on to India's plains.

3

Let the song go round the earth!
  Lands where Islam's sway
Darkly broods o'er home and hearth
  Cast their bonds away!
Let His praise from Afric's shore
Rise and swell her wide lands o'er!

4

Let the song go round the earth
  Where the summer smiles;
Let the notes of holy mirth
  Break from distant isles!
Inland forests, dark and dim,
Icebound coasts give back the hymn.

5

Let the song go round the earth,
  Jesus Christ is King!
With the story of His worth
  Let the whole world ring!
Him creation all adore
Evermore and evermore.

191

From Greenland's Icy Mountains

Missionary Hymn—7. 6. 7. 6. D.

Reginald Heber, 1819   Lowell Mason, 1824

1 From Green-land's i - cy moun-tains, From In-dia's cor-al strand,

Where Af-ric's sun-ny foun-tains Roll down their gold-en sand;

From man-y an an-cient riv-er, From man-y a palm-y plain,

They call us to de - liv - er Their land from er - ror's chain.

<table>
<tr><td>

2

What though the spicy breezes
  Blow soft o'er Ceylon's isle;
Though ev'ry prospect pleases
  And only man is vile;
In vain with lavish kindness
  The gifts of God are strown;
The heathen in his blindness
  Bows down to wood and stone.

</td><td>

3

Can we whose souls are lighted
  With wisdom from on high,
Can we to men benighted
  The lamp of life deny?
Salvation! Oh, Salvation!
  The joyful sound proclaim
Till each remotest nation
  Has learned Messiah's name.

</td></tr>
</table>

4

Waft, waft, ye winds, His story,
And you, ye waters, roll,
Till like a sea of glory
It spreads from pole to pole;
Till o'er our ransomed nature
The Lamb for sinners slain,
Redeemer, King, Creator,
In bliss returns to reign.

192

Dear Savior, Bless the Children

Christus, der ist mein—7. 6. 7. 6.

Author unknown   Melchior Vulpius, 1609

1 Dear Sav-ior, bless the chil-dren Who've gath-ered here to-day.

Oh, send Thy Ho-ly Spir-it, And teach us how to pray.

2

Dear Lord, wilt Thou not help us
Obey Thy great command,
And send Thy blessed Gospel
Abroad through ev'ry land?

3

May missionaries carry
The message of Thy love,
The wonderful salvation
Christ brought us from above.

4

Lord, bless the work we're doing;
Oh, bless our gifts, though small;
And hear our prayer for His sake
Who died to save us all.

193

Hark! the Voice of Jesus Crying

Galilean—8. 7. 8. 7. D.

St. 1, 2, 4, Daniel March, 1868
St. 3, author unknown

Joseph Barnby, 1883

1. Hark! the voice of Jesus cry-ing, "Who will go and work to-day?

Fields are white and har-vests wait-ing, Who will bear the sheaves a-way?"

Loud and long the Mas-ter call-eth, Rich re-ward He of-fers thee;

Who will an-swer, glad-ly say-ing, "Here am I, send me, send me"?

2

If you cannot speak like angels,
  If you cannot preach like Paul,
You can tell the love of Jesus,
  You can say He died for all.
If you cannot rouse the wicked
  With the Judgment's dread alarms,
You can lead the little children
  To the Savior's waiting arms.

3

If you cannot be a watchman,
  Standing high on Zion's wall,
Pointing out the path to heaven,
  Off'ring life and peace to all,
With your prayers and with your
      bounties
  You can do what God demands;
You can be like faithful Aaron,
  Holding up the prophet's hands.

4

Let none hear you idly saying,
"There is nothing I can do,"
While the souls of men are dying
And the Master calls for you.
Take the task He gives you gladly,
Let His work your pleasure be;
Answer quickly when He calleth,
"Here am I, send me. send me!"

194

Soldiers of the Cross, Arise

Gott sei Dank—7. 7. 7. 7.

William W. How, 1854, alt., ab.

"Neues geistreiches Gesangbuch"
Halle, 1704

1 Sol-diers of the Cross, a-rise, Gird you with your ar-mor bright.

Might-y are your en-e-mies, Hard the bat-tle ye must fight.

2

O'er a faithless, fallen world
  Raise your banner in the sky;
Let it float there wide unfurled;
  Bear it onward, lift it high.

3

Mid the homes of want and woe,
  Strangers to the living Word,
Let the Savior's heralds go,
  Let the voice of hope be heard.

4

To the weary and the worn
  Tell of realms where sorrows cease;
To the outcast and forlorn
  Speak of mercy and of peace.

5

Be the banner still unfurled,
  Still unsheathed the Spirit's Sword;
Spread Thy Word in all the world;
  Let Thy kingdom come, O Lord.

195

O Christ, Our True and Only Light

O Jesu Christ, mein's—L. M.

Johann Heermann, 1630
Tr., Catherine Winkworth, 1858, alt.   "Nuernbergisches Gesangbuch," 1676

1 O Christ, our true and on-ly Light, En-light-en those who sit in night; Let those a-far now hear Thy voice And in Thy fold with us re-joice.

2
Fill with the radiance of Thy grace
The souls now lost in error's maze
And all whom in their secret minds
Some dark delusion haunts and blinds.

3
Oh, gently call those gone astray
That they may find the saving way!
Let ev'ry conscience sore opprest
In Thee find peace and heav'nly rest.

4
Oh. make the deaf to hear Thy Word,
And teach the dumb to speak, dear
   Lord,
Who dare not yet the faith avow,
Though secretly they hold it now.

5
Shine on the darkened and the cold,
Recall the wanderers to Thy fold,
Unite all those who walk apart,
Confirm the weak and doubting heart.

6
So they with us may evermore
Such grace with wondering thanks
   adore
And endless praise to Thee be given
By all Thy Church in earth and
   heaven.

Jesus Shall Reign Where'er the Sun

Duke Street—L. M.

Isaac Watts, 1719, cento

John Hatton, 1793

1 Je - sus shall reign wher - e'er the sun Does his suc - ces - sive jour - neys run, His king-dom stretch from shore to shore Till moons shall wax and wane no more.

2
For Him shall endless prayer be
    made,
And endless praises crown His head;
His name, like sweet perfume, shall
    rise
With ev'ry morning sacrifice.

3
People and realms of ev'ry tongue
Dwell on His love with sweetest
    song;
And infant voices shall proclaim
Their early blessings on His name.

4
Blessings abound where'er He reigns;
The pris'ner leaps, unloosed his
    chains,
The weary find eternal rest,
And all the sons of want are blest.

5
Where He displays His healing
    power,
Death and the curse are known no
    more;
In Him the tribes of Adam boast
More blessings than their father lost.

6
Let every creature rise and bring
Peculiar honors to our King;
Angels descend with songs again,
And earth repeat the loud Amen.

197

O Zion, Haste, Thy Mission High Fulfilling

Angelic Songs—11. 10. 11. 10., with Refrain

Mary Ann Thomson, 1834-1923   James Walch, 1837-1901

1 O Zi - on, haste, thy mis - sion high ful - fill - ing,

To tell to all the world that God is Light,

That He who made all na - tions is not will - ing

One soul should per - ish, lost in shades of night.

Pub - lish glad ti - dings, ti - dings of peace,

Ti - dings of Je - sus, re - demp-tion and re -lease.

2

Behold how many thousands still are lying
   Bound in the darksome prison house of sin,
With none to tell them of the Savior's dying,
   Or of the life He died for them to win.
Publish glad tidings, tidings of peace,
Tidings of Jesus, redemption and release.

3

Proclaim to ev'ry people, tongue, and nation
   That God, in whom they live and move, is Love;
Tell how He stooped to save His lost creation
   And died on earth that man might live above.
Publish glad tidings, tidings of peace,
Tidings of Jesus, redemption and release.

I Love to Tell the Story

Hankey — 7. 6. 7. 6. D., with Refrain

Katherine Hankey, 1834-1911   William G. Fischer, 1835-1912

1 I love to tell the sto-ry Of un-seen things a-bove,

Of Je-sus and His glo-ry, Of Je-sus and His love.

I love to tell the sto-ry, Be-cause I know 'tis true;

It sa-tis-fies my long-ings As noth-ing else can do.

Refrain

I love to tell the sto-ry 'Twill be my theme in glo-ry,

To tell the old, old sto-ry Of Je-sus and His love.

2

I love to tell the story;
  'Tis pleasant to repeat
What seems, each time I tell it,
  More wonderfully sweet.
I love to tell the story;
  For some have never heard
The message of salvation
  From God's own holy Word.

Refrain.

3

I love to tell the story;
  For those who know it best
Seem hungering and thirsting
  To hear it like the rest.
And when, in scenes of glory,
  I sing the new, new song,
'Twill be the old, old story
  That I have loved so long.

Refrain.

199

Oh, Still in Accents Sweet and Strong

St. Flavian—C. M.

Samuel Longfellow, 1819-1892

"Psalter"
John Day, 1562

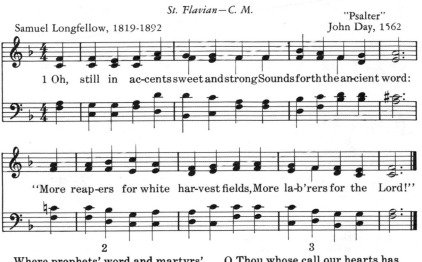

1 Oh, still in ac-cents sweet and strong Sounds forth the an-cient word:

"More reap-ers for white har-vest fields, More la-b'rers for the Lord!"

2

Where prophets' word and martyrs'
    blood
  And pray'rs of saints were sown,
We, to their labors ent'ring in,
  Would reap where they have
    strown.

3

O Thou whose call our hearts has
    stirred,
  To do Thy will we come,
Thrust in our sickles at Thy word,
  And bear our harvest home.

200

The Morning Light Is Breaking

Webb—7. 6. 7. 6. D.

Samuel F. Smith, 1832   George J. Webb, 1837

1 The morn-ing light is break-ing, The dark-ness dis-ap-pears;

The sons of earth are wak-ing To pen-i-ten-tial tears.

Each breeze that sweeps the o-cean Brings ti-dings from a-far

Of na-tions in com-mo-tion, Pre-pared for Zi-on's war.

2
See heathen nations bending
  Before the God we love
And thousand hearts ascending
  In gratitude above,
While sinners, now confessing,
  The Gospel call obey
And seek the Savior's blessing,
  A nation in a day.

3
Blest river of salvation,
  Pursue thine onward way;
Flow thou to ev'ry nation
  Nor in thy richness stay;
Stay not till all the lowly
  Triumphant reach their home;
Stay not till all the holy
  Proclaim, "The Lord is come."

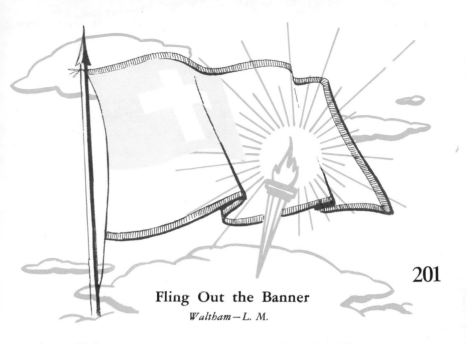

Fling Out the Banner

Waltham — L. M.

George W. Doane, 1799-1859   J. Baptiste Calkin, 1827-1905

1 Fling out the ban-ner! Let it float Sky-ward and sea-ward, high and wide;

The sun, that lights its shin-ing folds, The Cross, on which the Sav-ior died.

2

Fling out the banner! Heathen lands
Shall see from far the glorious
sight,
And nations, crowding to be born,
Baptize their spirits in its light.

3

Fling out the banner! Let it float
Skyward and seaward high and
wide;
Our glory, only in the Cross;
Our only hope, the Crucified!

Send Thou, O Lord, to Every Place

Isleworth—8. 8. 8. 6.

Mary C. Gates, 1888   Samuel Howard, †1782

1 Send Thou, O Lord, to ev-'ry place Swift mes-sen-gers be-fore Thy face, The her-alds of Thy won-drous grace, Where Thou Thy-self wilt come.

2
Send men whose eyes have seen the
  King,
Men in whose ears His sweet words
  ring;
Send such Thy lost ones home to
  bring;
  Send them where Thou wilt come—

3
To bring good news to souls in sin,
The bruised and broken hearts to win;
In every place to bring them in
  Where Thou Thyself wilt come.

4
Thou who hast died, Thy vict'ry
  claim;
Assert, O Christ,Thy glory's name
And far to lands of pagan shame
  Send men where Thou wilt come.

5
Gird each one with the Spirit's Sword,
The sword of Thine own deathless
  Word,
And make them conquerors, conquer-
  ing Lord,
  Where Thou Thyself wilt come.

6
Raise up, O Lord the Holy Ghost,
From this broad land a mighty host;
Their war cry, "We will seek the lost
  Where Thou, O Christ, wilt come."

Spread, Oh, Spread, Thou Mighty Word

Hoechster Priester—7. 7. 7. 7.

Jonathan F. Bahnmeier, 1827, ab.
Tr., Catherine Winkworth, 1858, alt.

"Musikalischer Christenschatz"
Basel, 1745

1 Spread, oh, spread, thou might-y Word, Spread the
king-dom of the Lord, Where-so-e'er His
breath has giv'n Life to be-ings meant for heav'n.

2
Tell them how the Father's will
Made the world and keeps it still,
How His only Son He gave
Man from sin and death to save.

3
Tell of our Redeemer's love,
Who forever doth remove
By His holy sacrifice
All the guilt that on us lies.

4
Tell them of the Spirit giv'n
Now to guide us up to heav'n,
Strong and holy, just and true,
Working both to will and do.

5
Up! The ripening fields ye see.
Mighty shall the harvest be;
But the reapers still are few,
Great the work they have to do.

6
Lord of Harvest, let there be
Joy and strength to work for Thee
Till the nations far and near
See Thy light and learn Thy fear.

Arise, O God, and Shine

Darwall's 148th—6. 6. 6. 6. 8. 8.

William Hurn, 1813   John Darwall, 1770

1 Arise, O God, and shine In all Thy saving might, And prosper each design To spread Thy glorious light; Let healing streams of mercy flow That all the earth Thy truth may know.

2

Bring distant nations near
  To sing Thy glorious praise;
Let ev'ry people hear
  And learn Thy holy ways.
Reign, mighty God, assert Thy cause,
And govern by Thy righteous laws.

3

To God, the only Wise,
  The one immortal King,
Let hallelujahs rise
  From ev'ry living thing;
Let all that breathe, on ev'ry coast,
Praise Father, Son, and Holy Ghost.

205

There Is a Happy Land

Happy Land—Irregular

A. Young, 1807-1889   "Select Melodies," 1827

1 There is a hap-py land Far, far a-way, Where saints in glo-ry stand, Bright, bright as day. Oh, how they sweet-ly sing: Wor-thy is the Sav-ior King, Loud let His prais-es ring, Praise, praise, for aye!

2

Come to that happy land,
  Come, come away;
Why will ye doubting stand,
  Why still delay?
Oh, we shall happy be,
When, from sin and sorrow free,
Lord, we shall live with Thee,
  Blest, blest for aye.

3

Bright, in that happy land
  Beams every eye;
Kept by a Father's hand,
  Love cannot die.
Oh, then, to glory run,
Where, a crown and kingdom won,
And, bright above the sun,
  We reign for aye.

I'm But a Stranger Here

Heaven Is My Home—6. 4. 6. 4. 6. 6. 6. 4.

T. R. Taylor, 1836, alt.   Arthur S. Sullivan, 1872

1 I'm but a stran-ger here, Heav'n is my home;

Earth is a des-ert drear, Heav'n is my home.

Dan-ger and sor-row stand Round me on ev-'ry hand;

Heav'n is my fa-ther-land, Heav'n is my home.

2

What though the tempest rage,
  Heav'n is my home;
Short is my pilgrimage,
  Heav'n is my home;
And time's wild wintry blast
Soon shall be over past;
I shall reach home at last,
  Heav'n is my home.

3

There at my Savior's side
  Heav'n is my home;
I shall be glorified,
  Heav'n is my home.
There are the good and blest,
Those I love most and best;
And there I, too, shall rest,
  Heav'n is my home.

4
Therefore I murmur not,
Heav'n is my home;
Whate'er my earthly lot,
Heav'n is my home;
And I shall surely stand
There at my Lord's right hand.
Heav'n is my fatherland,
Heav'n is my home.

207

Jerusalem, My Happy Home

St. Peter—C. M.

F. B. P., c. 1580
Cento 1801, alt.

Alexander R. Reinagle, 1836

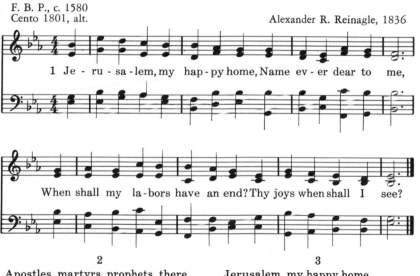

1 Je - ru - sa - lem, my hap - py home, Name ev - er dear to me,

When shall my la - bors have an end? Thy joys when shall I see?

2
Apostles, martyrs, prophets, there
  Around my Savior stand;
And soon my friends in Christ below
  Will join the glorious band.

3
Jerusalem, my happy home,
  When shall I come to thee?
When shall my labors have an end?
  Thy joys when shall I see?

4
O Christ, do Thou my soul prepare
For that bright home of love
That I may see Thee and adore
With all Thy saints above.

208

In Heaven Above, In Heaven Above

In Heaven Above—8. 6. 8. 6. 8. 8. 6.

Laurentius Laurentii, 1573-1655
Tr., William MacCall, 1868

Norwegian folk tune

1 In heav'n a - bove, in heav'n a - bove, Where God, our Fa - ther, dwells, How bound - less there the bless - ed - ness! No tongue its great - ness tells; There face to face, and full and free, For - ev - er, ev - er

more we see Our God, the Lord of Hosts!

2

In heav'n above, in heav'n above,
  What glory deep and bright!
The splendor of the noonday sun
  Grows pale before its light.
The heav'nly light that ne'er goes
    down,
Around whose radiance clouds ne'er
    frown,
  Is God, the Lord of Hosts.

3

In heav'n above, in heav'n above,
  No tears of pain are shed;
For none can yonder fade or die;
  Life's fullness round is spread,
And like an ocean, joy o'erflows,
And with immortal mercy glows
  Our God, the Lord of Hosts.

4

In heav'n above, in heav'n above,
  God hath a joy prepared
Which human ear had never heard
  Nor human vision shared,
Which never entered human breast,
By human lips was ne'er expressed,
  O God, the Lord of Hosts!

There's a Friend for Little Children

Shelter—8. 6. 7. 6. 7. 6. 7. 6.

Albert Midlane, 1859

Samuel Smith, 1874

1 There's a Friend for lit-tle chil-dren A-bove the bright blue sky,
A Friend who nev-er chang-es, Whose love will nev-er die;
Un-like our friends by na-ture Who change with chang-ing years,
This Friend is al-ways wor-thy The pre-cious name He bears.

2
There's a home for little children
  Above the bright blue sky,
Where Jesus reigns in glory,
  A home of peace and joy;
No home on earth is like it
  Nor can with it compare,
For everyone is happy
  Nor can be happier there.

3
There's a crown for little children
  Above the bright blue sky,
And all who look to Jesus,
  Shall wear it by and by,
A crown of brightest glory
  Which He shall there bestow
On all who love the Savior
  And walk with Him below.

Jerusalem the Golden

Ewing—7. 6. 7. 6. D.

Bernard of Morlas, c. 1140, cento
Tr., John M. Neale, 1849

Alexander Ewing, 1853

1 Je - ru - sa - lem the gold - en, With milk and hon - ey blest,

Be - neath thy con-tem - pla - tion Sink heart and voice op - prest.

I know not, oh, I know not, What joys a - wait us there,

What ra-dian-cy of glo - ry, What bliss be -yond com - pare.

2
There is the throne of David;
  And there, from care released,
The shout of them that triumph,
  The song of them that feast;
And they who with their Leader
  Have conquered in the fight
Forever and forever
  Are clad in robes of white.

3
O sweet and blessed country,
  The home of God's elect!
O sweet and blessed country
  That eager hearts expect!
Jesus, in mercy brings us
  To that dear land of rest,
Who art, with God the Father
  And Spirit, ever blest.

Around the Throne of God in Heaven

Children's Praises—C. M., with Refrain

Anne H. Shepherd, 1836   Arr. by Henry E. Matthews

1 A-round the throne of God in heav'n Thou-sands of chil-dren stand,

Chil-dren whose sins are all for-giv'n, A ho-ly, hap-py band,

Sing-ing: "Glo-ry, glo-ry, Glo-ry be to God on high."

2
In flowing robes of spotless white
  See everyone arrayed;
Dwelling in everlasting light
  And joys that never fade,
    Singing: "Glory be to God on
    high."

3
What brought them to that world
  above,
  That heav'n so bright and fair,
Where all is peace and joy and love;
  How came those children there,
    Singing: "Glory be to God on
    high"?

4
Because the Savior shed His blood
  To wash away their sin;
Bathed in that pure and precious flood,
  Behold them white and clean,
    Singing: "Glory be to God on
    high."

5
On earth they sought the Savior's
  grace,
  On earth they loved His name,
So now they see His blessèd face
  And stand before the Lamb,
    Singing: "Glory be to God on
    high."

212

I Am Baptized - O Blessed Day

Pentecost—L. M.

A. C. Mueller, 1948

William Boyd, 1847-1928

1 I am bap - tized — O bless - ed day On which my sins were washed a - way, When Heav-en's grace up - on me smiled And I be - came God's ho - ly child.

2

Oh, let me daily help receive
Thy word of pardon to believe;
When I am tempted, make me strong
To choose the right and hate the
    wrong.

3

So will I keep the promise given
When I was made an heir of heaven,
My Savior joyfully confess,
And serve the Lord in holiness.

Music copyright by Novello and Company, Ltd. Used by permission.

Jesus Took the Babes and Blessed Them

Vesper Hymn—8. 7. 8. 7. D.

Matthias Loy, 1828-1915

Russian folk song

1 Je-sus took the babes and blessed them Brought to Him in days of old;

Fond-ly in His arms ca-ressed them, Bade them welcome to His fold.

Oh, what love the Sav-ior showed them, When in faith they came to Him!

Oh, what love the Sav-ior showed them, When in faith they came to Him!

2

Thus today we come to Jesus
When in Baptism we are brought;
And He blesses and receives us
When His Word to us is taught.
Lord, what mercy Thou dost show us!
Keep us steadfast in Thy faith!
Lord, what mercy Thou dost show us!
Keep us steadfast in Thy faith!

He That Believes and Is Baptized

Es ist das Heil—8. 7. 8. 7. 8. 8. 7.

Thomas Kingo, 1689
Tr., George T. Rygh, 1909

German melody, c. 1400

1 He that believes and is baptized
Shall see the Lord's salvation;
Baptized into the death of Christ,
He is a new creation.
Through Christ's redemption he shall stand
Among the glorious heav'nly band
Of ev'ry tribe and nation.

2

With one accord, O God, we pray:
 Grant us Thy Holy Spirit;
Look Thou on our infirmity
 Through Jesus' blood and merit.
Grant us to grow in grace each day
That by this Sacrament we may
 Eternal life inherit.

215

I Was Made a Christian

Adoro te devote — 6. 5. 6. 5. D.

French proper melody
Arr. by Paul G. Bunjes, 1954

John Samuel Jones, c. 1880

1 I was made a Chris - tian When my name was giv'n,

One of God's dear chil - dren And an heir of heav'n.

In the name of Chris - tian I will glo - ry now,

Ev-er-more re-mem-ber My bap-tis-mal vow.

2
I must, like a Christian,
  Shun all evil ways,
Keep my faith in Jesus,
  Serve Him all my days.
Called to be a Christian,
  I will praise the Lord,
Seek for His assistance
  So to keep my word.

3
All a Christian's blessings
  I will claim for mine:
Holy work and worship,
  Fellowship divine.
Father, Son, and Spirit,
  Give me grace that I
Now may live a Christian,
  And a Christian die.

216

A Holy Mystery Is Here

St. Crispin—L. M.

Matthias Loy, 1880, cento, alt.

George J. Elvey, 1862

1 A ho-ly mys-ter-y is here To chal-lenge faith and wak-en fear: The Sav-ior comes as food di-vine, Con-cealed in earth-ly bread and wine.

2

This world is loveless; but above,
What wondrous boundlessness of
    love!
The King of Glory stoops to me
My spirit's life and strength to be.

3

In consecrated wine and bread
No eye perceives the myst'ry dread;
But Jesus' words are strong and
    clear:
"My body and My blood are here."

4

Lord, show us still that Thou art good,
And grant us evermore this food.
Give faith to every wav'ring soul,
And make each wounded spirit whole.

O Bread of Life from Heaven

O Welt, ich muss dich lassen — 7. 7. 6. 7. 7. 8.

Latin, Anonymous, 1661
Tr., Philip Schaff, 1869

Heinrich Isaac, 1490

1 O Bread of life from heav-en, To wea-ry pil-grims giv—en, O Man-na from a-bove: The souls that hun-ger feed Thou, The hearts that seek Thee lead Thou With Thy most sweet and ten-der love.

2
O Fount of grace redeeming,
O River ever streaming
 From Jesus' holy side:
Come, Thou, Thyself bestowing
On thirsting souls, and flowing
 Till all their wants are satisfied.

3
O Lord, this feast receiving,
Thy Word of truth believing,
 We Thee unseen adore:
Grant, when our life is ended,
That we, to heav'n ascended,
 May see Thy glory evermore.

Let Thy Blood in Mercy Poured

Jesus, meine Zuversicht—7. 8. 7. 8. 7. 7.

Greek; tr., John Brownlie, 1907   Johann Crueger, 1656

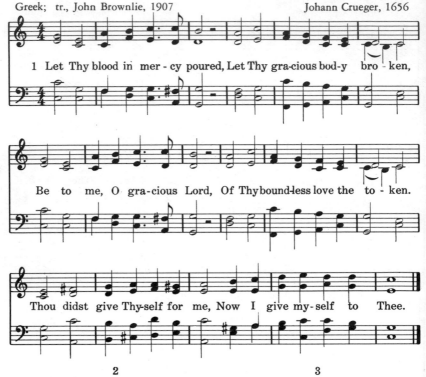

1 Let Thy blood in mer - cy poured, Let Thy gra-cious bod-y bro - ken,

Be to me, O gra-cious Lord, Of Thy bound-less love the to - ken.

Thou didst give Thy-self for me, Now I give my-self to Thee.

2

Thou didst die that I might live;
  Blessed Lord, Thou cam'st to save
  me;
All that love of God could give
  Jesus by His sorrows gave me.
Thou didst give Thyself for me,
Now I give myself to Thee.

3

By the thorns that crowned Thy brow,
  By the spear wound and the nailing,
By the pain and death, I now
  Claim, O Christ, Thy love unfailing.
Thou didst give Thyself for me,
Now I give myself to Thee.

4

Wilt Thou own the gift I bring?
  All my penitence I give Thee;
Thou art my exalted King,
  By Thy matchless love forgive me.
Thou didst give Thyself for me,
Now I give myself to Thee.

The NATION

219

Lord, While for All Mankind We Pray

St. Flavian—C. M.

John R. Wreford, 1837, ab., alt.

"Psalter"
John Day, 1562

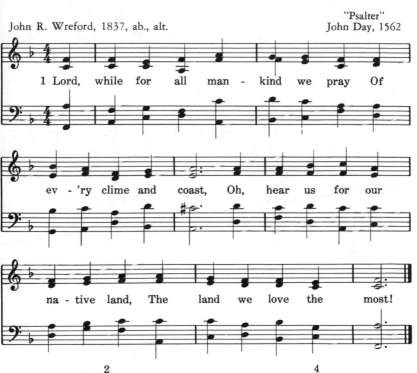

1 Lord, while for all man - kind we pray Of ev - 'ry clime and coast, Oh, hear us for our na - tive land, The land we love the most!

2

Oh, guard our shores from ev'ry foe,
  With peace our borders bless,
With prosp'rous times our cities
    crown,
  Our fields with plenteousness!

3

Unite us in the sacred love
  Of knowledge, truth, and Thee;
And let our hills and valleys shout
  The songs of liberty.

4

Here may Thy Gospel, pure and mild,
  Smile on our Sabbath hours
And piety and virtue bless
  Our fathers' home and ours.

5

Lord of the nations, thus to Thee
  Our country we commend.
Be Thou her Refuge and her Trust,
  Her everlasting Friend.

God Bless Our Native Land

America—6. 6. 4. 6. 6. 6. 4.

Tr., Charles T. Brooks, 1834
Tr., John S. Dwight, 1844

"Thesaurus Musicus," 1740

1 God bless our na-tive land! Firm may she ev-er stand Through storm and night! When the wild tem-pests rave, Rul-er of wind and wave, Do Thou our coun-try save By Thy great might.

2
For her our prayer shall rise
To God above the skies;
On Him we wait.
Thou who art ever nigh,
Guarding with watchful eye,
To Thee aloud we cry,
God save the State!

221

My Country, 'Tis of Thee

1
My country, 'tis of thee,
Sweet land of liberty,
Of thee I sing;
Land where my fathers died,
Land of the pilgrims' pride,
From ev'ry mountainside
Let freedom ring.

2
Our fathers' God, to Thee,
Author of liberty,
To Thee we sing.
Long may our land be bright
With freedom's holy light;
Protect us by Thy might,
Great God, our King!

God of Our Fathers

National Hymn—10. 10. 10. 10.

Daniel C. Roberts, 1841-1907   George Warren, 1828-1902

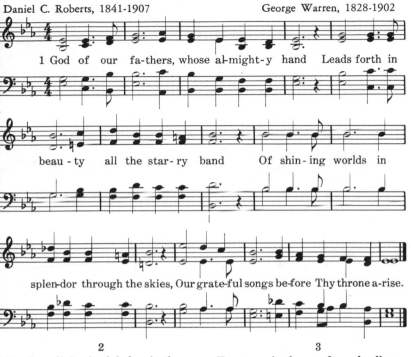

1 God of our fa-thers, whose al-might-y hand Leads forth in
beau-ty all the star-ry band Of shin-ing worlds in
splen-dor through the skies, Our grate-ful songs be-fore Thy throne a-rise.

2

Thy love divine hath led us in the
    past,
In this free land by Thee our lot is
    cast;
Be Thou our Ruler, Guardian, Guide,
    and Stay,
Thy Word our Law, Thy paths our
    chosen way.

3

From war's alarms, from deadly
    pestilence,
Be Thy strong arm our ever sure
    defense;
Thy true religion in our hearts
    increase,
Thy bounteous goodness nourish us
    in peace.

4

Refresh Thy people on their toilsome
    way,
Lead us from night to never-ending
    day;
Fill all our lives with love and grace
    divine,
And glory, laud, and praise be ever
    Thine.

223

Swell the Anthem, Raise the Song

St. George—7. 7. 7. 7. D.

Nathan Strong, 1799

George J. Elvey, 1858

1 Swell the an-them, raise the song; Prais-es to our God be-long.

Saints and an-gels join to sing Prais-es to the heav'n-ly King.

Bless-ings from His lib-'ral hand Flow a-round this hap-py land.

Kept by Him, no foes an-noy; Peace and free-dom we en-joy.

2

Here, beneath a peaceful sway,
May we cheerfully obey,
Never feel oppression's rod,
Ever own and worship God.
Hark, the voice of nature sings
Praises to the King of Kings.
Let us join the choral song
And the grateful notes prolong.

224

Abide, O Dearest Jesus

Christus, der ist mein—7. 6. 7. 6.

Josua Stegmann, 1628
Tr., August Crull, †1923

Melchior Vulpius, 1609

1 A-bide, O dear-est Je-sus, A-mong us with Thy grace
That Sa-tan may not harm us Nor we to sin give place.

2

Abide, O dear Redeemer,
　Among us with Thy Word,
And thus now and hereafter
　True peace and joy afford.

3

Abide with heav'nly brightness
　Among us, precious Light;
Thy truth direct and keep us
　From error's gloomy night.

4

Abide with richest blessings
　Among us, bounteous Lord;
Let us in grace and wisdom
　Grow daily through Thy Word.

5

Abide with Thy protection
　Among us, Lord our Strength,
Lest world and Satan fell us
　And overcome at length.

6

Abide, O faithful Savior,
　Among us with Thy love;
Grant steadfastness, and help us
　To reach our home above.

Faith of Our Fathers! Living Still

St. Catherine—8. 8. 8. 8. 8. 8.

Henri F. Hemy, 1818-1888
Alt. by James G. Walton, 1821-1905

Frederick William Faber, 1814-1863

1 Faith of our fa - thers! liv - ing still In spite of dun-geon, fire, and sword! Oh, how our hearts beat high with joy When-e'er we hear that glo - rious word: Faith of our fa - thers, ho - ly faith, We will be true to thee till death.

2
Faith of our fathers! God's great
  power
  Shall win all nations unto thee;
And through the truth that comes
  from God
  Mankind shall then be truly free.
Faith of our fathers, holy faith,
We will be true to thee till death.

3
Faith of our fathers! We will love
  Both friend and foe in all our strife
And preach thee, too, as love knows
  how
  By kindly words and virtuous life.
Faith of our fathers, holy faith,
We will be true to thee till death.

Oh, Take My Hand, Dear Savior

Oh, Take My Hand—7. 4. 7. 4. D.

Julia von Hautzmann, d. 1901
Tr., composite 1925, alt.

Friedrich Silcher, 1789-1860

1 Oh, take my hand, dear Sav - ior, And lead Thou me,
Till at my jour-ney's end - ing I dwell with Thee.
A - lone I dare not jour - ney One sin - gle day,
So do Thou guide my foot-steps On life's rough way.

2

Thou mighty God of Ages,
　Oh, be Thou near;
When angry tempest rages,
　I need not fear.
Close by Thy side abiding,
　I fear no foe;
While Thy strong hand is guiding,
　Life hath no woe.

3

When evening's shadows lengthen,
　The night is come,
My faint heart, Savior, strengthen,
　And bring me home.
Take Thou my hand and lead me
　Unto the end;
In life and death I need Thee,
　O blessed Friend!

All Depends on Our Possessing

Alles ist an Gottes Segen—8. 8. 7. 8. 8. 7.

Author unknown, c. 1673
Tr., Catherine Winkworth, 1858, alt., cento

Johann B. Koenig, 1738

1 All de-pends on our pos-sess-ing God's a-bun-dant grace and bless-ing, Though all earth-ly wealth de-part. He who trusts with faith un-shak-en In his God is not for-sak-en And e'er keeps a daunt-less heart.

2
He who hitherto hath fed me
And to many joys hath led me,
 Is and ever shall be mine.
He who did so gently school me,
He who still doth guide and rule me,
 Will remain my Help divine.

3
Many spend their lives in fretting
Over trifles and in getting
 Things that have no solid ground.
I shall strive to win a treasure
That will bring me lasting pleasure
 And that now is seldom found.

4

Well He knows what best to grant me;
All the longing hopes that haunt me,
Joy and sorrow, have their day.
I shall doubt His wisdom never—
As God wills, so be it ever—
I to Him commit my way.

228

Lord Jesus, Thou Art Mine

Potsdam—S. M.

Edward Sill, 1841-1887   "Church Psalter," 1854

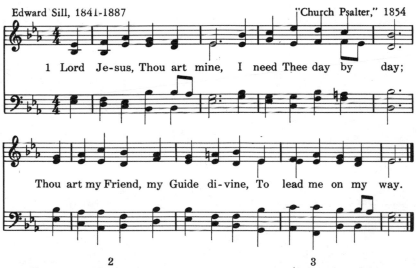

1 Lord Jesus, Thou art mine, I need Thee day by day;

Thou art my Friend, my Guide divine, To lead me on my way.

2

Lord Jesus, Thou art mine,
  I need Thy strength and power;
Thou art the Vine, I am the branch,
  Protect me every hour.

3

Lord Jesus, Thou art mine,
  I need Thy saving grace;
Oh, let Thy face upon me shine
  Until my dying days.

4

Lord Jesus, Thou art mine,
  I need Thy tender love,
For Thou art mine, and I am Thine,
  Here and at home above.

Guide Me, O Thou Great Jehovah

Guide Me—8. 7. 8. 7. 4. 7.

William Williams, 1745
Tr., William and Peter Williams, 1771-1772

George W. Warren, 1884

1 Guide me, O Thou great Je-ho-vah, Pil-grim through this bar-ren land. I am weak, but Thou art might-y; Hold me with Thy pow'r-ful hand. Bread of heav-en, Feed me till I want no more.

2

Open now the crystal fountain
　Whence the healing stream doth
　　flow;
Let the fiery, cloudy pillar
　Lead me all my journey through.
Strong Deliv'rer,
　Be Thou still my Strength and
　　Shield.

3

When I tread the verge of Jordan,
　Bid my anxious fears subside;
Death of death and hell's Destruction,
　Land me safe on Canaan's side.
Song of praises
　I will ever give to Thee.

Today Thy Mercy Calls Us

Anthes—7. 6. 7. 6. D.

Oswald Allen, 1861, ab.

Friedrich K. Anthes, 1847

1 To - day Thy mer-cy calls us To wash a-way our sin.

How - ev - er great our tres-pass, What-ev - er we have been,

How - ev - er long from mer - cy Our hearts have turned a - way,

Thy pre-cious blood can cleanse us And make us white to - day.

2
Today Thy gate is open,
　And all who enter in
Shall find a Father's welcome
　And pardon for their sin.
The past shall be forgotten,
　A present joy be giv'n,
A future grace be promised,
　A glorious crown in heav'n.

3
Today our Father calls us,
　His Holy Spirit waits;
His blessed angels gather
　Around the heav'nly gates.
No question will be asked us
　How often we have come;
Although we oft have wandered,
　It is our Father's home.

231

There Is a Fountain Filled with Blood

First Tune—Horsley—C. M.

William Cowper, 1771, cento

William Horsley, 1844

1 There is a foun-tain filled with blood Drawn from Im-man-uel's veins, And sin-ners plunged be-neath that flood Lose all their guilt-y stains.

2

The dying thief rejoiced to see
That fountain in his day;
And there have I, as vile as he,
Washed all my sins away.

3

Dear dying Lamb, Thy precious blood
Shall never lose its power
Till all the ransomed Church of God
Be saved to sin no more.

4

E'er since by faith I saw the stream
Thy flowing wounds supply,
Redeeming love has been my theme
And shall be till I die.

5

When this poor lisping, stammering
tongue
Lies silent in the grave,
Then in a nobler, sweeter song
I'll sing Thy power to save.

There Is a Fountain Filled with Blood

Second Tune—Cowper—C. M.

William Cowper, 1771, cento

Lowell Mason, 1830

1 There is a foun-tain filled with blood Drawn from Im-man-uel's

veins, And sin-ners plunged be - neath that flood Lose

all their guilt - y stains, Lose all their guilt-y stains.

All Glory Be to God on High

Allein Gott in der Hoeh'—8. 7. 8. 7. 8. 8. 7.

Nikolaus Decius, 1525
Tr., Catherine Winkworth, 1863, alt.

Nikolaus Decius, 1539, asc.

1 All glo-ry be to God on high, Who hath our race be-friend-ed! To us no harm shall now come nigh, The strife at last is end-ed. God show-eth His good will to men, And peace shall reign on earth a-gain; Oh, thank Him for His good-ness!

2
We praise, we worship Thee, we trust,
  And give Thee thanks forever,
O Father, that Thy rule is just
  And wise and changes never.
Thy boundless pow'r o'er all things
    reigns,
Done is whate'er Thy will ordains:
  Well for us that Thou rulest.

3
O Jesus Christ, Thou only Son
  Of God, Thy heav'nly Father,
Who didst for all our sins atone
  And Thy lost sheep dost gather:
Thou Lamb of God, to Thee on high
From out our depths we sinners cry,
  Have mercy on us, Jesus!

4

O Holy Ghost, Thou precious Gift,
  Thou Comforter unfailing,
O'er Satan's snares our souls uplift,
  And let Thy pow'r availing
Avert our woes and calm our dread.
For us the Savior's blood was shed;
  We trust in Thee to save us.

233

In the Cross of Christ I Glory

Rathbun—8. 7. 8. 7.

John Bowring, 1825   Ithamar Conkey, 1849

1 In the Cross of Christ I glo-ry, Tow'r-ing o'er the wrecks of time.

All the light of sa - cred sto-ry Ga-thers round its head sub-lime.

2
When the woes of life o'ertake me,
  Hopes deceive, and fears annoy,
Never shall the Cross forsake me;
  Lo, it glows with peace and joy.

3
When the sun of bliss is beaming
  Light and love upon my way,
From the Cross the radiance
    streaming
Adds more luster to the day.

4
Bane and blessing, pain and pleasure,
  By the Cross are sanctified;
Peace is there that knows no measure,
  Joys that through all time abide.

All Glory, Laud, and Honor

Valet will ich dir geben—7. 6. 7. 6. D.

St. Theodulph of Orleans, c. 820
Tr., John M. Neale, 1854, alt.

Melchior Teschner, 1613

1 All glo-ry, laud, and hon-or To Thee, Re-deem-er, King,

To whom the lips of chil-dren Made sweet ho-san-nas ring.

Thou art the King of Is-rael, Thou Da-vid's roy-al Son,

Who in the Lord's name com-est, The King and Bless-ed One.

2
All glory, laud, and honor
  To Thee, Redeemer, King,
To whom the lips of children
  Made sweet hosannas ring.
The company of angels
  Are praising Thee on high,
And mortal men and all things
  Created make reply.

3
All glory, laud, and honor
  To Thee, Redeemer, King,
To whom the lips of children
  Made sweet hosannas ring.
The people of the Hebrews
  With palms before Thee went;
Our praise and prayer and anthems
  Before Thee we present.

4

All glory, laud, and honor
  To Thee, Redeemer, King,
To whom the lips of children
  Made sweet hosannas ring.
To Thee, before Thy Passion,
  They sang their hymns of praise;
To Thee, now high exalted,
  Our melody we raise.

5

All glory, laud, and honor
  To Thee, Redeemer, King,
To whom the lips of children
  Made sweet hosannas ring.
Thou didst accept their praises;
  Accept the prayers we bring,
Who in all good delightest,
  Thou good and gracious King.

235

Our God, Our Help in Ages Past

St. Anne—C. M.

Isaac Watts, 1719, cento   William Croft, 1708

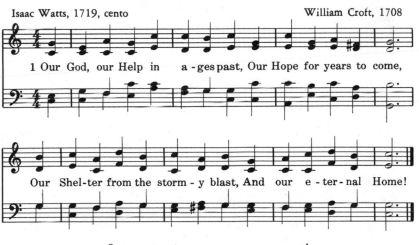

1 Our God, our Help in a-ges past, Our Hope for years to come,

Our Shel-ter from the storm-y blast, And our e-ter-nal Home!

2

Under the shadow of Thy throne
  Thy saints have dwelt secure;
Sufficient is Thine arm alone,
  And our defense is sure.

3

Before the hills in order stood
  Or earth received her frame,
From everlasting Thou art God,
  To endless years the same.

4

A thousand ages in Thy sight
  Are like an evening gone,
Short as the watch that ends the night
  Before the rising sun.

5

Our God, our Help in ages past,
  Our Hope for years to come,
Be Thou our Guard while troubles last
  And our eternal Home!

Just as I Am, Without One Plea

First Tune—St. Crispin—L. M.

Charlotte Elliott, 1836   George J. Elvey, 1862

1 Just as I am, with-out one plea But that Thy

blood was shed for me And that Thou bidd'st me

come to Thee, O Lamb of God, I come, I come.

2

Just as I am and waiting not
To rid my soul of one dark blot,
To Thee, whose blood can cleanse
    each spot,
    O Lamb of God, I come, I come.

3

Just as I am, though tossed about
With many a conflict, many a doubt,
Fightings and fears within, without,
    O Lamb of God, I come, I come.

4

Just as I am, poor, wretched, blind;
Sight, riches, healing of the mind,
Yea, all I need, in Thee to find,
    O Lamb of God, I come, I come.

5

Just as I am, Thou wilt receive,
Wilt welcome, pardon, cleanse,
    relieve;
Because Thy promise I believe,
    O Lamb of God, I come, I come.

6

Just as I am; Thy love unknown
Has broken every barrier down.
Now to be Thine, yea, Thine alone,
    O Lamb of God, I come, I come.

Just as I Am, Without One Plea

Second Tune—Woodworth—L. M.

Charlotte Elliott, 1836   William B. Bradbury, 1849

1 Just as I am, with-out one plea But that Thy blood was shed for me And that Thou bidd'st me come to Thee, O Lamb of God, I come, I come.

2

Just as I am and waiting not
To rid my soul of one dark blot,
To Thee, whose blood can cleanse
    each spot,
    O Lamb of God, I come, I come.

3

Just as I am, though tossed about
With many a conflict, many a doubt,
Fightings and fears within, without,
    O Lamb of God, I come, I come.

4

Just as I am, poor, wretched, blind;
Sight, riches, healing of the mind,
Yea, all I need, in Thee to find,
    O Lamb of God, I come, I come.

5

Just as I am, Thou wilt receive,
Wilt welcome, pardon, cleanse,
    relieve;
Because Thy promise I believe,
    O Lamb of God, I come, I come.

6

Just as I am; Thy love unknown
Has broken every barrier down.
Now to be Thine, yea, Thine alone,
    O Lamb of God, I come, I come.

Rejoice, Ye Pure in Heart

Marion—S. M., with Refrain

Edward H. Plumptre, 1865   Arthur H. Messiter, 1883

1 Re-joice, ye pure in heart, Re-joice, give thanks, and sing;

Your fes-tal ban-ner wave on high, The cross of Christ, your King.

Re-joice, Re-joice, Re-joice, give thanks and sing!

2
Bright youth and snow-crowned age,
　Strong men and maidens fair,
Raise high your free, exulting song,
　God's wondrous praise declare.
Rejoice, rejoice,
Rejoice, give thanks and sing!

3
Yes, on through life's long path,
　Still chanting as ye go,
From youth to age, by night and day,
　In gladness and in woe,
Rejoice, rejoice,
Rejoice, give thanks and sing!

4
Still lift your standard high,
　Still march in firm array,
As warriors through the darkness toil,
　Till dawns the golden day.
Rejoice, rejoice,
Rejoice, give thanks and sing!

Around the Throne of God a Band

Winchester New—L. M.

John M. Neale, 1842, cento

"Musikalisches Handbuch"
Hamburg, 1690

1 A - round the throne of God a band Of glo - rious an - gels ev - er stand; Bright things they see, sweet harps they hold, And on their heads are crowns of gold.

2

Some wait around Him, ready still
To sing His praise and do His will;
And some, when He commands them, go
To guard His servants here below.

3

Lord, give Thy angels ev'ry day
Command to guide us on our way,
And bid them ev'ry evening keep
Their watch around us while we sleep

4

So shall no wicked thing draw near
To do us harm or cause us fear;
And we shall dwell, when life is past,
With angels round Thy throne at last.

Hosanna, Loud Hosanna

Ellacombe—7. 6. 7. 6. D.

Jeannette Threlfall, 1873

"Gesangbuch d. Herzogl. Wuerttemberg. Hofkapelle," 1784

1 Ho-san-na, loud ho-san-na, The lit-tle chil-dren sang;
Through pil-lared court and Tem-ple The love-ly an-them rang.
To Je-sus, who had blessed them, Close fold-ed to His breast,
The chil-dren sang their prais-es, The sim-plest and the best.

2
From Olivet they followed
Mid an exultant crowd,
The victor palm branch waving
And chanting clear and loud.
The Lord of men and angels
Rode on in lowly state
Nor scorned that little children
Should on His bidding wait.

3
"Hosanna in the highest!"
That ancient song we sing,
For Christ is our Redeemer,
The Lord of heav'n our King.
Oh, may we ever praise Him
With heart and life and voice
And in His blissful presence
Eternally rejoice!

Oh, Sing a Song of Bethlehem

Kingsfold—C. M. D.

English traditional melody
Arr. by Ralph Vaughan Williams, 1906

Louis F. Benson, 1899

1 Oh, sing a song of Beth-le-hem, Of shep-herds watch-ing there
And of the news that came to them From an-gels in the air.
The light that shone on Beth-le-hem Fills all the world to-day;
Of Je-sus' birth and peace on earth The an-gels sing al-way.

2

Oh, sing a song of Nazareth,
  Of sunny days of joy,
Oh, sing of fragrant flowers' breath
  And of the sinless Boy;
For now the flowers of Nazareth
  In ev'ry heart may grow;
Now spreads the fame of His dear
    name
  On all the winds that blow.

3

Oh, sing a song of Galilee,
  Of lake and woods and hill,
Of Him who walked upon the sea
  And bade its waves be still;
For though like waves on Galilee,
  Dark seas of trouble roll,
When faith has heard the Master's
    word,
  Falls peace upon the soul.

Tune from *The English Hymnal*. Used by permission of the Oxford University Press.

241

We Sing the Praise of Him Who Died

O Jesu Christ, mein's—L. M.

Thomas Kelly, 1815, ab.   "Nuernbergisches Gesangbuch," 1676

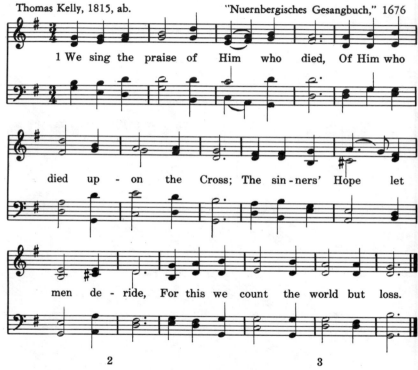

1 We sing the praise of Him who died, Of Him who

died up - on the Cross; The sin-ners' Hope let

men de - ride, For this we count the world but loss.

2

Inscribed upon that Cross we see
　In shining letters "God is Love."
He bears our sins upon the tree,
　He brings us mercy from above.

3

The Cross!—it takes our guilt away,
　It holds the fainting spirit up,
It cheers with hope the gloomy day
　And sweetens ev'ry bitter cup.

4

It makes the coward spirit brave
　And nerves the feeble arm for fight;
It takes all terror from the grave
　And gilds the bed of death with
　　light.

From All That Dwell Below the Skies

Lasst uns erfreuen—L. M., with Alleluias

"Geistliche Kirchengesaeng"
Cologne, 1623

Isaac Watts, 1719

1 From all that dwell be-low the skies Let the Cre-a-tor's praise a-rise; Al-le - lu - ia! Al-le-lu - ia! Let the Re-deem-er's name be sung Through ev-'ry land, by ev-'ry tongue. Al-le - lu - ia! Al-le-lu - ia! Al-le - lu - ia! Al-le - lu - ia! Al-le - lu - ia!

2
Eternal are Thy mercies, Lord;
 Eternal truth attends Thy Word:
 Alleluia! Alleluia!
Thy praise shall sound from shore to
 shore
Till suns shall rise and set no more.
 Alleluia! Alleluia!
 Alleluia! Alleluia! Alleluia!

Jesus, I My Cross Have Taken

Hyfrydol—8. 7. 8. 7. D.

Henry Francis Lyte, 1824, cento

Rowland H. Prichard, 1855, alt.

1 Je-sus, I my cross have tak-en, All to leave and fol-low Thee;

Des - ti - tute, de-spised, for - sak - en, Thou from hence my All shalt be.

Per-ish ev-'ry fond am - bi - tion, All I've sought or hoped or known;

Yet how rich is my con-di-tion! God and heav'n are still mine own.

2

Let the world despise and leave me,
    They have left my Savior, too.
Human hearts and looks deceive me;
    Thou art not, like them, untrue.
And while Thou shalt smile upon me,
    God of wisdom, love, and might,
Foes may hate and friends may shun
    me;
    Show Thy face, and all is bright.

3

Take, my soul, thy full salvation;
    Rise o'er sin and fear and care.
Joy to find in every station,
    Something still to do or bear.
Think what Spirit dwells within thee,
    What a Father's smile is thine,
What a Savior died to win thee;
    Child of heaven, shouldst thou
    repine?

4

Haste, then, on from grace to glory,
  Armed by faith and winged by
    prayer;
Heaven's eternal day's before thee,
  God's own hand shall guide thee
    there.
Soon shall close the earthly mission,
  Swift shall pass thy pilgrim days,
Hope soon change to glad fruition,
  Faith to sight, and prayer to praise.

244

Thine Forever, God of Love

Vienna—7. 7. 7. 7.

Mary F. Maude, 1847, cento   Justin H. Knecht, 1797

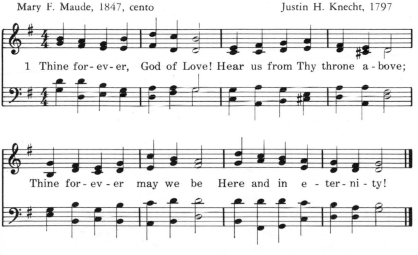

1 Thine for - ev - er, God of Love! Hear us from Thy throne a - bove;

Thine for - ev - er may we be Here and in e - ter - ni - ty!

2

Thine forever! Oh, how blest
They who find in Thee their rest!
Savior, Guardian, heav'nly Friend,
Oh, defend us to the end!

3

Thine forever, Lord of Life!
Shield us through our earthly strife.
Thou, the Life, the Truth, the Way,
Guide us to the realms of day.

4

Thine forever! Shepherd, keep
These Thy frail and trembling sheep.
Safe alone beneath Thy care,
Let us all Thy goodness share.

5

Thine forever! Thou our Guide,
All our wants by Thee supplied,
All our sins by Thee forgiven;
Lead us, Lord, from earth to heaven.

245

God, My Father, Loving Me

Light Divine—7. 7. 7. 7.

George W. Briggs, 1875

Orlando Gibbons, 1623

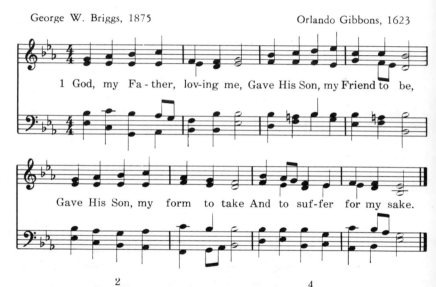

1 God, my Fa-ther, lov-ing me, Gave His Son, my Friend to be,

Gave His Son, my form to take And to suf-fer for my sake.

2
Jesus still remains the same
As in days of old He came.
As my Brother by my side
Still He seeks my steps to guide.

3
How can I repay Thy love,
Lord of all the hosts above?
What have I, a child, to bring
Unto Thee, Thou heav'nly King?

4
I have but myself to give;
Let me to Thy glory live;
Let me follow day by day
Thee, the true and living Way.

5
Then, when I am called to share
Yonder home Thou didst prepare,
I shall meet my King and praise
Him through everlasting days.

Words from *Songs of Praise.* Copyright 1931 Oxford University Press.
Used by permission.

Lord, I Confess Thy Tender Care

Tallis' Ordinal—C. M.

Jane Taylor, 1783-1824, alt.

Thomas Tallis, c. 1561

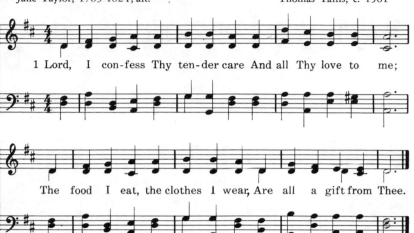

1 Lord, I con-fess Thy ten-der care And all Thy love to me;

The food I eat, the clothes I wear, Are all a gift from Thee.

2
'Tis Thou who keepest me from death
  And dangers every hour;
I cannot draw another breath
  Unless Thou give me power.

3
My health and friends and parents
    dear
  To me by God are given;
I have not any blessing here
  But what is sent from heaven.

4
Kind angels guard me every night,
  As round my bed they stay;
Nor am I absent from Thy sight
  In darkness or by day.

5
Such goodness, Lord, and constant
    care
  A child can ne'er repay;
But may it be my daily prayer
  To love Thee and obey.

Above the Clear, Blue Sky

Darwall's 148th—6. 6. 6. 6. 8. 8.

John Chandler, 1841   John Darwall, 1770

1 A-bove the clear, blue sky, In heav-en's bright a - bode, The
an-gel host on high Sing prais-es to their God. Al - le - lu -
ia! They love to sing To God, their King. Al - le - lu - ia!

2

But God from children's tongues
  On earth receiveth praise;
We, then, our cheerful songs
  In sweet accord will raise.
Alleluia!
  We, too, will sing
  To God, our King.
Alleluia!

3

O blessed Lord, Thy truth
  To all Thy flock impart,
And teach us in our youth
  To know Thee as Thou art.
Alleluia!
  Then shall we sing
  To God, our King.
Alleluia!

4

Oh, may Thy holy Word
  Spread all the world around;
And all with one accord
  Uplift the joyful sound.
Alleluia!
  All then shall sing
  To God, our King.
Alleluia!

Jesus, Tender Savior

St. Mary Magdalene—6. 5. 6. 5. D.

The New Sunday School Hymn Book, 1863   John B. Dykes, 1862

1 Je - sus, ten - der Sav - ior, Thou hast died for me;
Make me ver - y thank - ful In my heart to Thee.
When the sad, sad sto - ry Of Thy grief I read,
Make me ver - y sor - ry For my sins in - deed.

2

Now I know Thou livest
And dost plead for me;
Make me very thankful
In my prayers to Thee.
Soon I hope in glory
At Thy side to stand;
Make me fit to meet Thee
In that happy land.

All Things Bright and Beautiful

Royal Oak—7. 6. 7. 6., with Refrain

Cecil Frances Alexander, 1823-1895

English traditional melody
Ad. by Martin Shaw

1 All things bright and beau-ti-ful, All crea-tures great and small,

All things wise and won-der-ful, The Lord God made them all.

Fine

2 Each lit-tle flower that o-pens, Each lit-tle bird that sings,   He

D.C.

made their glow-ing col - ors, He made their ti - ny wings:

3
The purple-headed mountain,
  The river running by,
The sunset and the morning
  That brightens up the sky:
(Repeat the first stanza.)

4
The cold wind in the winter,
  The pleasant summer sun,
The ripe fruits in the garden,
  He made them everyone:
(Repeat the first stanza.)

5
The tall trees in the greenwood,
  The meadows for our play,
The rushes by the water
  To gather every day:
(Repeat the first stanza.)

6
He gave us eyes to see them,
  And lips that we might tell
How great is God Almighty,
  Who has made all things well:
(Repeat the first stanza.)

I Lay My Sins on Jesus

Aurelia—7. 6. 7. 6. D.

Horatius Bonar, 1843   Samuel S. Wesley, 1864

1 I lay my sins on Je-sus, The spot-less Lamb of God;
He bears them all and frees us From the ac-curs-ed load.
I bring my guilt to Je-sus To wash my crim-son stains
White in His blood most pre-cious Till not a spot re-mains.

2
I lay my wants on Jesus,
    All fullness dwells in Him;
He healeth my diseases,
    He doth my soul redeem.
I lay my griefs on Jesus,
    My burdens and my cares;
He from them all releases,
    He all my sorrows shares.

3
I rest my soul on Jesus,
    This weary soul of mine;
His right hand me embraces,
    I on His breast recline.
I love the name of Jesus,
    Immanuel, Christ, the Lord;
Like fragrance on the breezes
    His name abroad is poured.

4

I long to be like Jesus,
　Meek, loving, lowly, mild;
I long to be like Jesus,
　The Father's holy Child.
I long to be with Jesus
　Amid the heav'nly throng
To sing with saints His praises,
　To learn the angels' song.

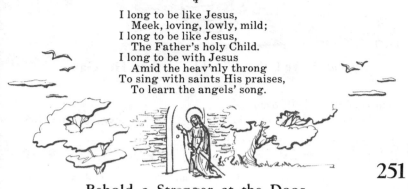

251

Behold a Stranger at the Door

Hamburg—L. M.

Joseph Grigg, 1765, cento

Based on First Gregorian Chant
Arr. by Lowell Mason, 1824

1 Behold a Stranger at the door! He gently knocks, has knocked be-fore,

Has wait-ed long, is　wait-ing still; You treat no oth-er friend so　ill.

2

But will He prove a friend indeed?
He will; the very Friend you need;
The Friend of sinners—yes, 'tis He,
With garments dyed on Calvary.

3

O lovely attitude! He stands
With melting heart and laden hands;
O matchless kindness! And He shows
This matchless kindness to His foes.

4

Admit Him lest His anger burn
And He, departing, ne'er return;
Admit Him, or the hour's at hand
When at His door denied you'll stand.

5

Oh, let the heavenly Stranger in,
Let in thy heart His reign begin.
Admit Him, open wide the door,
And He will bless thee evermore.

252

God Loved the World So that He Gave

St. Crispin—L. M.

Author unknown, 1791, cento
Tr., August Crull, †1923, alt.

George J. Elvey, 1862

1 God loved the world so that He gave His on-ly
Son the lost to save That all who would in
Him be-lieve Should ev-er-last-ing life re-ceive.

2

Christ Jesus is the Ground of faith,
Who was made flesh and suffered
    death;
All that confide in Him alone
Are built on this chief Cornerstone.

3

God would not have the sinner die,
His Son with saving grace is nigh,
His Spirit in the Word doth teach
How man the blessed goal may reach.

4

Be of good cheer, for God's own Son
Forgives all sins which thou hast
    done,
And, justified by Jesus' blood,
Thy Baptism grants the highest good.

Beautiful Savior

Schoenster Herr Jesu—5. 5. 7. 5. 5. 8.

Author unknown, 1677
Tr., Joseph A. Seiss, 1873

"Schlesische Volkslieder"
Leipzig, 1842

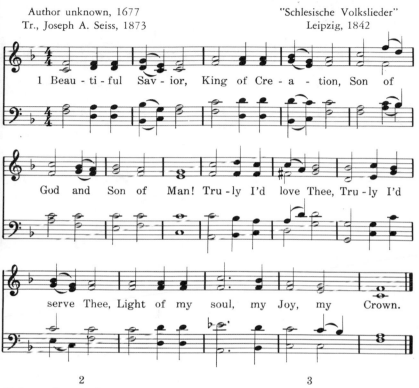

1 Beau - ti - ful Sav - ior, King of Cre - a - tion, Son of
God and Son of Man! Tru - ly I'd love Thee, Tru - ly I'd
serve Thee, Light of my soul, my Joy, my Crown.

2
Fair are the meadows,
Fair are the woodlands,
  Robed in flow'rs of blooming spring;
Jesus is fairer;
Jesus is purer;
  He makes our sorr'wing spirit sing.

3
Fair is the sunshine,
Fair is the moonlight,
  Bright the sparkling stars on high;
Jesus shines brighter,
Jesus shines purer,
  Than all the angels in the sky.

4
Beautiful Savior,
Lord of the nations,
  Son of God and Son of Man!
Glory and honor,
Praise, adoration,
  Now and forevermore be Thine!

Sun of My Soul, Thou Savior Dear

Hursley—L. M.

John Keble, 1820, cento

"Allgemeines Gesangbuch"
Vienna, 1775, ad.

1 Sun of my soul, Thou Sav - ior dear, It is not night if Thou be near. Oh, may no earth - born cloud a - rise To hide Thee from Thy serv - ant's eyes.

2

When the soft dews of kindly sleep
My wearied eyelids gently steep,
Be my last thought how sweet to rest
Forever on my Savior's breast.

3

Abide with me from morn till eve,
For without Thee I cannot live;
Abide with me when night is nigh,
For without Thee I dare not die.

4

If some poor wand'ring child of Thine
Has spurned today the voice divine,
Now, Lord, the gracious work begin;
Let him no more lie down in sin.

5

Watch by the sick; enrich the poor
With blessings from Thy boundless
        store;
Be every mourner's sleep tonight,
Like infant's slumbers, pure and light.

6

Come near and bless us when we wake,
Ere through the world our way we
        take,
Till in the ocean of Thy love
We lose ourselves in heaven above.

Humble Praises, Holy Jesus

Vesper Hymn—8.7.8.7.8.7.8.7.

Author unknown

Russian folk song

1 Hum-ble prais-es, ho-ly Je-sus, Chil-dren's voic-es raise to Thee;

In Thy mer-cy, oh, re-ceive us, Suf-fer us Thy lambs to be.

Refrain

Al-le-lu-ia, sweet-ly sing-ing, Joy-ful trib-ute now we bring.

Al - le-lu -ia! Al - le-lu-ia! Al - le-lu -ia to our King!

2
Gracious Savior, be Thou with us;
 Let Thy mercy richly flow;
Give Thy Spirit, blessed Jesus!
 Light and life on us bestow.
Alleluia, sweetly singing,
 Joyful tribute now we bring.
Alleluia! Alleluia!
 Alleluia to our King!

Drawn to the Cross, Which Thou Hast Blest

Dunstan—8. 8. 8. 6.

Genevieve M. Irons, 1880   Joseph Barnby, 1883

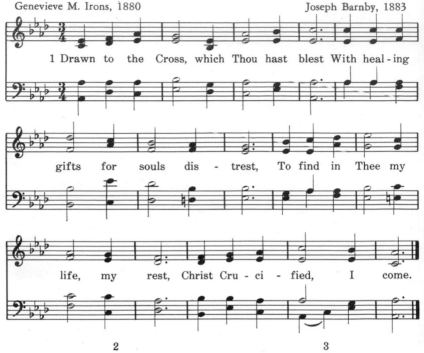

1 Drawn to the Cross, which Thou hast blest With heal-ing gifts for souls dis-trest, To find in Thee my life, my rest, Christ Cru-ci-fied, I come.

2

Thou knowest all my griefs and fears,
Thy grace abused, my misspent
    years;
Yet now to Thee with contrite tears,
    Christ Crucified, I come.

3

Wash me and take away each stain;
Let nothing of my sin remain.
For cleansing, though it be through
    pain,
    Christ Crucified, I come.

4

And then for work to do for Thee,
Which shall so sweet a service be
That angels well might envy me,
    Christ Crucified, I come.

May We Thy Precepts, Lord, Fulfill

Meribah—8. 8. 6. 8. 8. 6.

Edward Osler, 1836, alt.

Lowell Mason, 1839

1 May we Thy pre-cepts, Lord, ful - fill And do on earth our Fa-ther's will As an-gels do a-bove; Still walk in Christ, the liv-ing Way, With all Thy chil-dren and o - bey The law of Chris-tian love.

2
So may we join Thy name to bless,
Thy grace adore, Thy pow'r confess,
  From sin and strife to flee.
One is our calling, one our name,
The end of all our hopes the same,
  A crown of life with Thee.

3
Spirit of Life, of Love, and Peace,
Unite our hearts, our joy increase,
  Thy gracious help supply.
To each of us the blessing give
In Christian fellowship to live,
  In joyful hope to die.

Abide with Me! Fast Falls the Eventide

Eventide—10. 10. 10. 10.

Henry F. Lyte, 1847, cento

William H. Monk, 1861

1 A-bide with me! Fast falls the e-ven-tide; The dark-ness deep-ens; Lord, with me a-bide. When oth-er help-ers fail and com-forts flee, Help of the help-less, oh, a-bide with me!

2
Swift to its close ebbs out life's little day;
Earth's joys grow dim, its glories pass away;
Change and decay in all around I see.
O Thou, who changest not, abide with me!

3
I need Thy presence every passing hour;
What but Thy grace can foil the Tempter's power?
Who like Thyself my guide and stay can be?
Through cloud and sunshine, oh, abide with me!

4
I fear no foe, with Thee at hand to bless;
Ills have no weight and tears no bitterness.
Where is death's sting? where, grave, thy victory?
I triumph still if Thou abide with me.

5
Hold Thou Thy Cross before my closing eyes,
Shine through the gloom, and point me to the skies.
Heaven's morning breaks, and earth's vain shadows flee;
In life, in death, O Lord, abide with me!

Let Me Be Thine Forever

Ich dank' dir, lieber Herre—7. 6. 7. 6. D.

St. 1, Nikolaus Selnecker, 1572
St. 2, 3, author unknown, 1688
Tr., Matthias Loy, 1880, alt.

"Musika Deutsch"
Nuernberg, 1532

1 Let me be Thine for-ev-er, Thou faith-ful God and Lord;

Let me for-sake Thee nev-er Nor wan-der from Thy Word.

Lord, do not let me wa-ver, But give me stead-fast-ness,

And for such grace for-ev-er Thy ho-ly name I'll bless.

2
Lord Jesus, my Salvation,
 My Light, my Life divine,
My only Consolation,
 Oh, make me wholly Thine!
For Thou hast dearly bought me
 With blood and bitter pain.
Let me, since Thou hast sought me,
 Eternal life obtain.

3
And Thou, O Holy Spirit,
 My Comforter and Guide,
Grant that in Jesus' merit
 I always may confide,
Him to the end confessing
 Whom I have known by faith.
Give me Thy constant blessing,
 And grant a Christian death.

What a Friend We Have in Jesus

Friend—8. 7. 8. 7. D.

Joseph Scriven, 1865   Charles C. Converse, 1868

1 What a Friend we have in Je-sus, All our sins and griefs to bear!

What a priv-i-lege, to car-ry Ev-'ry-thing to God in prayer!

Oh, what peace we of-ten for-feit, Oh, what need-less pain we bear,

All be-cause we do not car-ry Ev-'ry-thing to God in prayer!

2	3
Have we trials and temptations?	Are we weak and heavy laden,
Is there trouble anywhere?	Cumbered with a load of care?
We should never be discouraged,	Precious Savior, still our Refuge—
Take it to the Lord in prayer.	Take it to the Lord in prayer.
Can we find a friend so faithful	Do thy friends despise, forsake thee?
Who will all our sorrows share?	Take it to the Lord in prayer;
Jesus knows our ev'ry weakness—	In His arms He'll take and shield thee,
Take it to the Lord in prayer.	Thou wilt find a solace there.

261

Jesus, Shepherd of the Sheep

Morgenglanz 7. 7. 7. 5.

Henry Cook, 1868

Friedrich Filitz, 1847, ad.

1 Je-sus, Shep-herd of the sheep, Who Thy Fa-ther's flock dost keep,
Safe we wake and safe we sleep, Guard-ed still by Thee.

2

In Thy promise firm we stand,
None can pluck us from Thy hand;
Speak—we hear—at Thy command
　We will follow Thee.

3

By Thy blood our souls were bought,
By Thy life salvation wrought,
By Thy light our feet are taught,
　Lord, to follow Thee.

Let Us Ever Walk with Jesus

Lasset uns mit Jesu ziehen—8. 7. 8. 7. 8. 7 7. 8. 7. 7.

Sigismund von Birken, 1653
Tr., J. Adam Rimbach, 1900

Georg G. Boltze, 1788

1 Let us ev-er walk with Je-sus, Fol-low His ex-am-ple pure,

Flee the world, which would de-ceive us And to sin our souls al-lure.

Ev-er in His foot-steps tread-ing, Bod-y here, yet soul a-bove,

Full of faith and hope and love, Let us do the Fa-ther's bid-ding.

Faith-ful Lord, a-bide with me, Sav-ior, lead, I fol-low Thee.

2

Let us gladly live with Jesus;
　Since He's risen from the dead,
Death and grave must soon release us,
　Jesus, Thou art now our Head,
We are truly Thine own members;
　Where Thou livest, there live we.
　Take and own us constantly,
Faithful Friend, as Thy dear brethren.
Jesus, here I live to Thee,
Also there eternally.

263

Loving Shepherd of Thy Sheep

Innocents—7. 7. 7. 7.

Jane E. Leeson, 1807-1882   French melody, 13th century

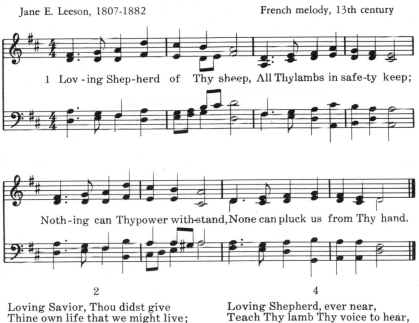

1 Lov-ing Shep-herd of Thy sheep, All Thy lambs in safe-ty keep;

Noth-ing can Thy power with-stand, None can pluck us from Thy hand.

2
Loving Savior, Thou didst give
Thine own life that we might live;
And the hands outstretched to bless
Bear the cruel nails' impress.

3
I would bless Thee every day,
Gladly all Thy will obey,
Like Thy blessed ones above,
Happy in Thy precious love.

4
Loving Shepherd, ever near,
Teach Thy lamb Thy voice to hear,
Suffer not my steps to stray
From the straight and narrow way.

5
Where Thou leadest, I would go,
Walking in Thy steps below,
Till before my Father's throne
I shall know as I am known.

264

Come, Children, and Join in Our Festival Song

Festival Song—11. 11. 11. 11.

Author unknown, cento   Composer unknown

1 Come, chil-dren, and join in our fes-ti-val song, And hail the sweet joys which this day brings a-long; We'll join our glad voic-es in one hymn of praise To God, who has kept us and length-ened our days.

2

Our Father in heaven, we lift up to Thee
Our voice of thanksgiving, our glad jubilee;
Oh, bless us, and guide us, dear Savior, we pray,
That from Thy blest precepts we never may stray.

3

And if, ere this glad year has drawn to a close,
Some loved one among us in death shall repose,
Grant, Lord, that the spirit in heaven may dwell,
In the bosom of Jesus, where all shall be well.

4

Kind teachers, we children would thank you this day
That faithfully, kindly, you've taught us the way
How we may escape from the world's sinful charms
And find a safe refuge in the Savior's loved arms.

5

And now, as we part, let us bid you good cheer,
We pray for a blessing on your labors here:
May many bright jewels be your blest reward
And crowns of rejoicing in the day of the Lord.

Children of the Heavenly King

Pleyel's Hymn—7. 7. 7. 7.

John Cennick, 1718-1755, cento

Ignaz J. Pleyel, 1757-1831

1 Chil-dren of the heav'n-ly King, As ye jour-ney, sweet-ly sing, Sing your Sav-ior's wor-thy praise, Glo-rious in His works and ways.

2
Lift your eyes, ye sons of light!
Zion's city is in sight;
There our endless home shall be,
There our Lord we soon shall see.

3
Fear not, children, joyful stand,
Led by His almighty hand;
Jesus Christ, your Father's Son,
Bids you undismayed go on.

4
Lord, obediently we go,
Gladly leaving all below;
Only, Lord, our Leader be,
That we still may follow Thee.

Nearer, My God, to Thee

Bethany—6. 4. 6. 4. 6. 6. 6. 4.

Sarah F. Adams, 1841, ab.   Lowell Mason, 1856

1 Near - er, my God, to Thee, Near - er to Thee.
E'en though it be a cross That rais - eth me,
Still all my song shall be, Near - er, my God, to Thee,
Near - er, my God, to Thee, Near - er to Thee.

2
Though like the wanderer,
  The sun gone down,
Darkness be over me,
  My rest a stone,
Yet in my dreams I'd be
Nearer, my God, to Thee,
Nearer, my God, to Thee,
Nearer to Thee.

3
There let my way appear
  Steps unto heav'n;
All that Thou sendest me
  In mercy giv'n;
Angels to beckon me
Nearer, my God, to Thee,
Nearer, my God, to Thee,
Nearer to Thee.

Come, Father, Son, and Holy Ghost

St. Magnus—8.6.8.6.

Charles Wesley, 1707-1788, alt.   Jeremiah Clark, 1709

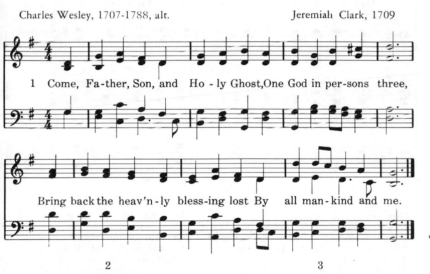

1 Come, Fa-ther, Son, and Ho - ly Ghost, One God in per-sons three,

Bring back the heav'n - ly bless-ing lost By all man - kind and me.

2
Eternal Sun of Righteousness,
  Display Thy beams divine,
And cause the glories of Thy face
  Upon my heart to shine.

3
Lift up Thy countenance serene,
  And let Thy happy child
Behold, without a cloud between,
  The Godhead reconciled.

4
Thy rich and loving peace bestow
  On me, through grace forgiven,
The joys of holiness below,
  And then the joys of heaven.

In Our Work and in Our Play

Ratisbon—7.7.7.7.7.7.

Whitefield G. Wills, alt.

"Saechsisches Choralbuch"
Leipzig, 1815

1 In our work and in our play, Je-sus, ev - er with us stay;

May we ev - er strive to be True and faith - ful un - to Thee.

Al - le - lu - ias loud we sing, We are chil - dren of the King.

2

May we in Thy strength subdue
Evil tempers, words untrue,
Thoughts impure, and deeds unkind,
All things hateful to Thy mind.
Alleluias loud we sing,
We are children of the King.

3

Children of the King are we!
May we loyal to Him be,
Try to please Him every day
In our work and in our play.
Alleluias loud we sing,
We are children of the King.

Jesus, from Thy Throne on High

Aus der Tiefe—7. 7. 7. 7.

Thomas B. Pollock, 1871   "Nürnbergisches Gesangbuch," 1676

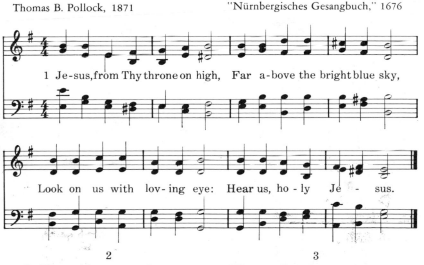

1 Je-sus, from Thy throne on high, Far a-bove the bright blue sky,
Look on us with lov-ing eye: Hear us, ho-ly Je - sus.

2	3

Be Thou with us every day
In our work and in our play;
When we learn and when we pray,
Hear us, holy Jesus.

When we lie asleep at night,
Ever may Thy angels bright
Keep us safe till morning light:
Hear us, holy Jesus.

Remember All the People

Far-off Lands — 7. 6. 7. 6. D.

Percy Dearmer, b. 1906   Melody of the Bohemian Brethren

1 Re-mem-ber all the peo-ple Who live in far-off lands,
In strange and lone-ly cit-ies, Or roam the des-ert sands,
Or farm the moun-tain pas-tures, Or till the end-less plains,
Where chil-dren wade through rice fields And watch the cam-el trains.

2
Some work in sultry forests
  Where apes swing to and fro,
Some fish in mighty rivers,
  Some hunt across the snow.
Remember all the children
  Who yet have never heard
The truth that comes from Jesus,
  The glory of His Word.

3
God bless the men and women
  Who serve Him oversea;
God raise up more to help them,
  To set the nations free,
Till all the distant people
  In every foreign place
Shall understand His kingdom
  And come into His grace.

How Wondrous and Great

Begone, Unbelief—10.10.11.11.

Henry U. Onderdonk, 1789-1858

Early American melody

How won-drous and great Thy works, God of praise!

How just, King of saints, and true are Thy ways!

Oh, who shall not fear Thee and hon-or Thy name?

Thou on-ly art ho-ly, Thou on-ly su - preme.

2
To nations long dark Thy light shall be shown;
Their worship and vows shall come to Thy throne;
Thy truth and Thy judgments shall spread all abroad,
Till earth's every people confess Thee their God.

Tune arrangement from *Hymns for Children and Grownups*. Used by permission.

O Jesu, Joy of Loving Hearts

Ach lieber Herre—8. 8. 8. 8. 6. 6.

From Jesu, dulcis memoria

Tr., Ray Palmer, 1859, alt.　　　　Arr. by Johannes Brahms, 1833-1897

1 O　Je - su, Joy of　lov - ing hearts, Thou Fount of Life, Thou

Light　of men, From　the best bliss that　earth im - parts　We

turn un - filled　to　Thee a - gain. O　Je - su,

Lord di - vine, Thy　love _____ with - in us shine.

2

Thy truth unchanged hath ever stood;
　Thou savest those that on Thee call;
To them that seek Thee Thou art good,
　To them that find Thee, All in all.
O Jesu, Lord divine,
Thy love within us shine.

3

O Jesu, ever with us stay;
　Make all our moments calm and
　　bright;
Chase the dark night of sin away;
　Shed o'er the world Thy holy light.
O Jesu, Lord divine,
Thy love within us shine.

When All Thy Mercies, O My God

Winchester Old—C. M.

Joseph Addison, 1712

"Psalter"
Thomas Este, 1592

1 When all Thy mer - cies, O my God, My
ris - ing soul sur - veys, Trans - port - ed with the
view, I'm lost In won - der, love, and praise.

2

Ten thousand thousand precious gifts
  My daily thanks employ;
Nor is the least a cheerful heart
  That tastes those gifts with joy.

3

Through ev'ry period of my life
  Thy goodness I'll pursue
And after death, in distant worlds,
  The glorious theme renew.

4

When nature fails and day and night
  Divide Thy works no more,
My ever grateful heart, O Lord,
  Thy mercies shall adore.

5

Through all eternity to Thee
  A joyful song I'll raise;
But, oh! eternity's too short
  To utter all Thy praise.

I Love God's Tiny Creatures

Forest Green — 7. 6. 8. 6. D.

English traditional melody
Arr. by R. Vaughan Williams, 1872 —

G. W. Briggs, 1875 —

1 I love God's ti-ny crea-tures That wan-der wild and free,

The cor-al-coat-ed la-dy bird, The vel-vet hum-ming bee.

Shy lit-tle flow'rs in hedge and dyke That hide them-selves a-way:

God paints them, though they are so small, God makes them bright and gay.

2

Dear Father, who hast all things made,
And carest for them all,
There's none too great for Thy great love
Nor anything too small:

If Thou canst spend such tender care
On things that grow so wild,
How wonderful Thy love must be
For me, Thy loving child!

From *Enlarged Songs of Praise.* Copyright 1931 by Oxford University Press.
Used by permission

275

I Am Jesus' Little Lamb

Weil ich Jesu Schaeflein bin—7. 7. 8. 8. 7. 7.

Henrietta L. von Hayn, 1778
Tr., composite

"Brueder Choral-Buch," 1784

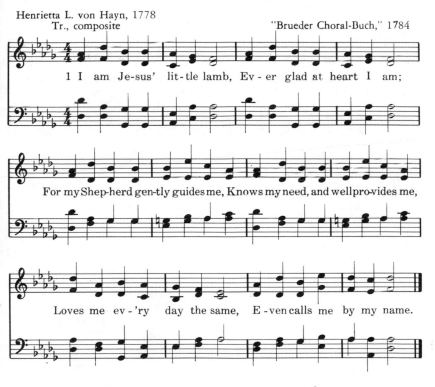

1 I am Je-sus' lit-tle lamb, Ev - er glad at heart I am;

For my Shep-herd gen-tly guides me, Knows my need, and well pro-vides me,

Loves me ev-'ry day the same, E -ven calls me by my name.

2
Day by day, at home, away,
Jesus is my Staff and Stay.
When I hunger, Jesus feeds me,
Into pleasant pastures leads me;
When I thirst, He bids me go
Where the quiet waters flow.

3
Who so happy as I am,
Even now the Shepherd's lamb?
And when my short life is ended,
By His angel host attended,
He shall fold me to His breast,
There within His arms to rest.

'Tis Jesus Loves the Little Ones

Little Ones—C. M.

Author unknown, ab.

Composer unknown

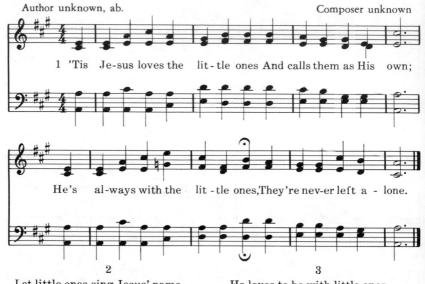

1 'Tis Je-sus loves the lit-tle ones And calls them as His own;

He's al-ways with the lit-tle ones, They're nev-er left a-lone.

2
Let little ones sing Jesus' name—
　He loves to hear them sing—
And fill His house with joyful sound
　And make His praises ring.

3
He loves to be with little ones
　And hear their childlike pray'r,
And tenderly He takes them up
　Into His loving care.

Jesus, Friend of Little Children

Westridge—8. 5. 8. 3.

Walter F. Mathams, 1882

Martin Shaw, 1875—

1 Je - sus, Friend of lit - tle chil-dren, Be a Friend to me;

Take my hand, and ev - er keep me Close to Thee.

2
Teach me how to grow in goodness,
  Daily as I grow;
Thou hast been a child, and surely
  Thou dost know.

3
Never leave me, nor forsake me;
  Ever be my Friend;
For I need Thee from life's dawning
  To its end.

From *Enlarged Songs of Praise.* By permission of the Oxford University Press.

Jesus Loves Me, Jesus Loves Me

Brocklesbury—8. 7. 8. 7.

Author unknown, alt.   Charlotte A. Barnard, 1868

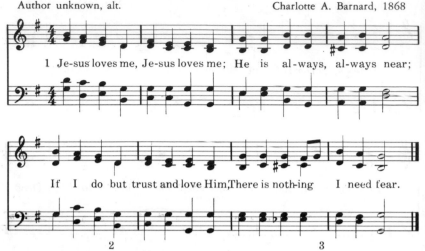

1 Je-sus loves me, Je-sus loves me; He is al-ways, al-ways near;

If I do but trust and love Him, There is noth-ing I need fear.

2   3
Jesus loves me; night and morning   Jesus loves me; and He watches
  Jesus hears the prayers I pray,   Over me with loving eye,
And He never, never leaves me   And He sends His holy angels
  When I work or when I play.   Safe to keep me till I die.

4
Jesus loves me; O Lord Jesus,
  Now I pray Thee by Thy love,
Keep me ever pure and holy,
  Till I come to Thee above.

279

There Is a Tender Shepherd

German Folk Tune—7. 6. 7. 6.

J. B. Cody   German folk tune

1 There is a ten-der Shep-herd Who watch-es o'er His sheep, And

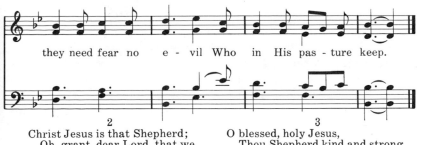

they need fear no e - vil Who in His pas - ture keep.

<table>
<tr><td>

2
Christ Jesus is that Shepherd;
  Oh, grant, dear Lord, that we
Within Thy pleasant pastures
  May safe and happy be!

</td><td>

3
O blessed, holy Jesus,
  Thou Shepherd kind and strong,
Thou Friend so true and loving,
  May we to Thee belong!

</td></tr>
</table>

4
Our only Hope of heaven,
  The Life, the Truth, the Way,
May we, with sins forgiven,
  Praise Thee in endless lay!

280

Jesus, Lead Me Day by Day

Posen—7. 7.7.7.

Author unknown   George C. Strattner

1 Je-sus, lead me day by day Ev - er in Thine own sweet way;

Teach me to be pure and true; Show me what I ought to do.

<table>
<tr><td>

2
When I'm tempted to do wrong,
Make me steadfast, wise, and strong;
And when all alone I stand,
Shield me with Thy mighty hand.

</td><td>

3
When my heart is glad and free,
Help me to remember Thee,
Happy most of all to know
That my Jesus loves me so.

</td></tr>
</table>

281

Gentle Jesus, Meek and Mild

Gentle Jesus—7. 7. 7. 7.

Charles Wesley, 1807-1888, alt.

Martin Shaw, 1876-

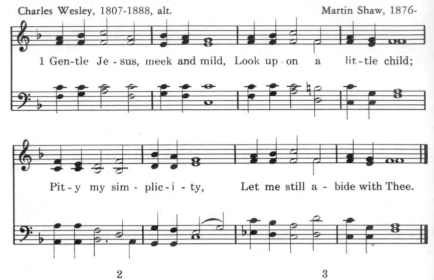

1 Gen-tle Je-sus, meek and mild, Look up-on a lit-tle child;

Pit-y my sim-plic-i-ty, Let me still a-bide with Thee.

2
Hold me fast in Thine embrace,
Let me see Thy smiling face;
Give me, Lord, Thy blessing give,
Keep me, Lord, and I shall live.

3
Lamb of God, I look to Thee,
Thou shalt my dear Savior be;
Thou art pitiful and kind,
Let me have Thy loving mind.

282

Who Made the Sky So Bright and Blue?

Who Made the Sky—C. M.

Author unknown

Composer unknown

1 Who made the sky so bright and blue? Who made the fields so green?

Who made the flow'rs that smell so sweet, In pret-ty col-ors seen?

2
Who made the birds to soar so high
And taught them how to sing?
Who made the pretty butterfly
And painted her bright wing?

3
'Twas God who made this world so fair,
The sun, the sky, the air;
'Twas God who made the sea, the ground,
And all the things around.

283

He Loves Me Too

Spring Song—C. M.

Author unknown   Composer unknown

1 Our heav'n-ly Fa-ther made the flow'rs, He paints them with per-fume.

If God so loves the lit-tle flow'rs, I know He loves me too.

2
Our heav'nly Father made the birds,
He shows them what to do;
If God so loves the little birds,
I know He loves me too.

3
God made the little birds and flow'rs
And all things large and small;
He'll not forget His little ones;
I know He loves them all.

God's a Father Kind and True

Spring Carol—7. 7. 7. 7.

A. C. Mueller, 1948

T. G. Stelzer, 1948
Harm. by Carl Halter

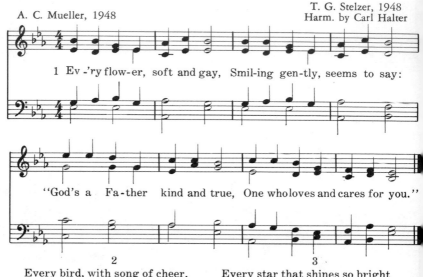

1 Ev-'ry flow-er, soft and gay, Smil-ing gent-ly, seems to say:

"God's a Fa-ther kind and true, One who loves and cares for you."

2
Every bird, with song of cheer,
Seems to carol sweet and clear:
"God's a Father kind and true,
One who loves and cares for you."

3
Every star that shines so bright
Seems to whisper through the night:
"God's a Father kind and true,
One who loves and cares for you."

4
Little children, every day
Raise your happy voice and say:
"God's a Father kind and true,
One who loves and cares for you."

285

Lord, Teach a Little Child to Pray

St. Flavian—C. M.

St. 1, Anonymous
St. 2, A. C. Mueller, 1954

"Psalter"
John Day, 1562

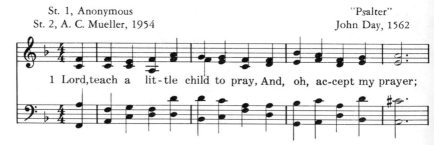

1 Lord, teach a lit-tle child to pray, And, oh, ac-cept my prayer;

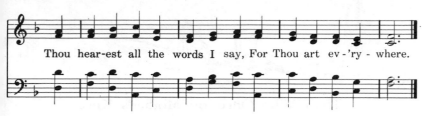

Thou hear-est all the words I say, For Thou art ev-'ry-where.

2

In Jesus' name, I pray Thee, Lord,
Wash all my sins away,
And help me, Savior, by Thy Word
To serve Thee day by day.

286

In the Early Morning

Naegeli—6. 5. 6. 5.

Author unknown   H. G. Naegeli

1 In the ear-ly morn-ing, With the sun's first rays,

All God's lit-tle chil-dren Thank and pray and praise.

2

I, too, thanks would offer,
Jesus, Shepherd dear,
For Thy tender pasture,
For Thy guiding care.

3

And I would implore Thee,
Be with me this day,
Lest I from Thee wander,
Into sin do stray.

4

In the hush of evening,
With the sun's last rays,
All God's little children
Thank and pray and praise.

287

Thou Who Once on Mother's Knee

David Valleau—7.7.7.7.7.7.

Francis T. Palgrave, 1824-1897   Harold W. Friedell, 1953

Thou who once on moth-er's knee Wast a lit-tle one like me,

When I wake or go to bed, Lay Thy hands up-on my head;

Let me feel Thee ver-y near, Je-sus Christ, our Sav-ior dear.

2
Be beside me in the light,
Be close by me through the night;
Make me gentle, kind, and true,
Do what I am bid to do;
Help and cheer me when I fret,
And forgive when I forget.

From *Hymns for Children and Grownups.* Copyright 1953 by Farrar, Straus, and Young. Used by permission of both composer and publisher.

Another Happy Birthday

Magdalena — 7. 6. 7. 6.

Kate T. Sizer, st. 2, alt.

German melody, 16th century
Harm. by Paul Bunjes, 1954

1 An - oth - er hap - py birth - day To
one of us is giv'n; Then let us thank the
Fa - ther For all His gifts from heav'n.

2
Oh, may the Savior's mercy
And love to *him* be near,
To keep *him* safe and happy
Through every coming year.

Words from *The Children's Hymnal and Service Book.* Used by permission of the Muhlenberg Press. Music set expressly for *The Children's Hymnal.*

We Are in God's House Today

Orientis partibus—7. 7. 7. 7.

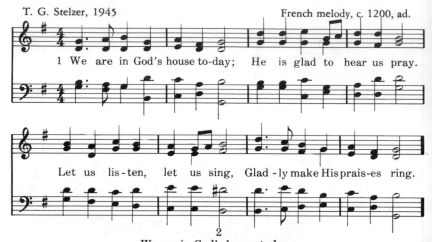

T. G. Stelzer, 1945   French melody, c. 1200, ad.

1 We are in God's house to-day; He is glad to hear us pray.

Let us lis-ten, let us sing, Glad-ly make His prais-es ring.

2
We are in God's house today;
He is glad to hear us pray.
Let us listen to His Word,
Gladly do what we have heard.

290   **Father, Bless Our School Today**

Gott sei Dank—7. 7. 7. 7.

Author unknown   "Neues geistreiches Gesangbuch"
               Halle, 1704

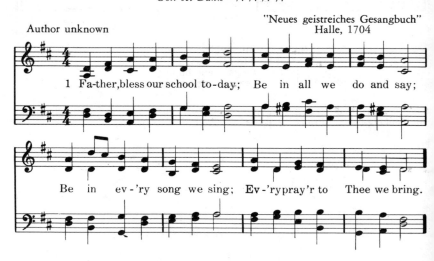

1 Fa-ther, bless our school to-day; Be in all we do and say;

Be in ev-'ry song we sing; Ev-'ry pray'r to Thee we bring.

2
Jesus, well-beloved Son,
May Thy will by us be done;
Come and meet with us today;
Teach us, Lord, Thyself, we pray.

3
Holy Spirit, Mighty Pow'r,
Consecrate this Lord's day hour;
Unto us Thy blessing give;
Touch our souls that we may live.

291

Let Me Learn of Jesus

Sandown—6. 5. 6. 5.

Fanny J. Crosby, 1820-1915

J. F. Swift

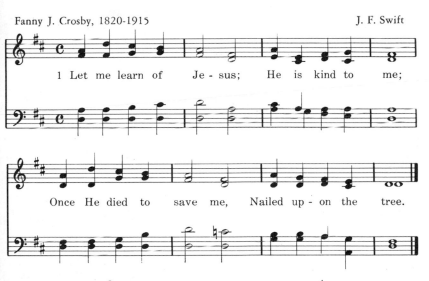

1 Let me learn of Je-sus; He is kind to me;
Once He died to save me, Nailed up-on the tree.

2
When I go to Jesus,
    He will hear me pray,
Make me pure and holy,
    Take my sins away.

3
Let me think of Jesus;
    He is full of love,
Looking down upon me
    From His throne above.

4
If I trust in Jesus,
    If I do His will,
Then I shall be happy,
    Safe from every ill.

5
Oh, how good is Jesus!
    May He hold my hand
And at last receive me
    To a better land.

Away in a Manger

First Tune—Cradle Song—11. 11. 11. 11.

American carol

William J. Kirkpatrick, 1838-1921

1 A-way in a man-ger, no crib for a bed,

The lit-tle Lord Je-sus laid down His sweet head;

The stars in the bright sky looked down where He lay,

The lit-tle Lord Je-sus, a-sleep on the hay.

2

The cattle are lowing, the Baby awakes,
But little Lord Jesus, no crying He makes.
I love Thee, Lord Jesus, look down from the sky,
And stay by my cradle till morning is nigh.

3

Be near me, Lord Jesus; I ask Thee to stay
Close by me forever, and love me, I pray.
Bless all the dear children in Thy tender care,
And fit us for heaven to live with Thee there.

Away in a Manger

Second Tune—Cradle Song—11. 11. 11. 11.

Traditional   Traditional

A - way in a man-ger, no crib for a bed, The lit-tle Lord

Je - sus laid down His sweet head; The stars in the sky looked

down where He lay, The lit - tle Lord Je-sus, a-sleep on the hay.

293

A Little Child on the Earth Has Been Born

Flemish Traditional Melody—10. 10. 11. 11.

Old Flemish carol
Tr., R. C. Trevelyan

Arr. by Julius Roentgen

1 A lit - tle Child on the earth has been born, A lit - tle Child on the earth has been born; He came to the earth for the sake of us all, He came to the earth for the sake of us all.

2
He came to earth, but no home did
  He find,
He came to earth, but no home did
  He find;
He came to the earth, and its cross
  did He bear,
He came to the earth, and its cross
  did He bear.

3
He came to earth for the sake of us
  all,
He came to earth for the sake of us
  all,
And wishes us all a happy new year,
And wishes us all a happy new year.

Come Ye All to Bethlehem

7. 7. 8. 8. 6. 7.

Slovak carol

Slovak carol
Arr. by Richard Kountz

1 Come ye all to Beth - le - hem, Where is born the King of men, Where the ho - ly In - fant sleep - eth, While her watch the moth - er keep - eth. Come all to Beth - le - hem, Where is born the King of men.

2
Come ye all to Bethlehem,
Where is born the King of men,
Where the hymns of joy, ascending,
Sound the Infant's praise unending.
Come all to Bethlehem,
Where is born the King of men.

295

Winds Through the Olive Trees

Christmas carol — 6. 4. 6. 4.

Author unknown   Richard T. Rohlfing, 1953

1 Winds through the ol - ive trees Soft - ly did blow

'Round lit - tle Beth - le - hem Long, long a - go.

2
Sheep on the hillside lay
  Whiter than snow,
Shepherds were watching them
  Long, long ago.

3
Then from the happy sky
  Angels bent low,
Singing their songs of joy
  Long, long ago.

4
For in a manger bed
  Cradled, we know,
Christ came to Bethlehem
  Long, long ago.

From *Echoes from Bethlehem.* Copyright 1954 by Concordia Publishing House

As Each Happy Christmas

Alle Jahre wieder—6. 5. 6. 5.

J. W. Hey
Tr., Mrs. Harriett H. Spaeth

Johann C. H. Rinck, 1770-1846

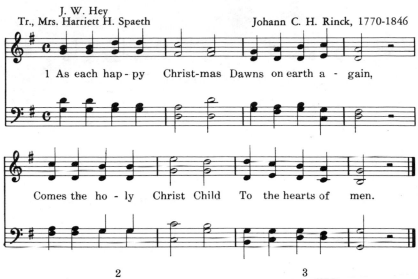

1 As each hap-py Christ-mas Dawns on earth a - gain,

Comes the ho - ly Christ Child To the hearts of men.

2
Enters with His blessing
Into ev'ry home,
Guides and guards our footsteps
As we go and come.

3
All unknown, beside me
He will ever stand
And will safely lead me
With His own right hand.

297

We Welcome Glad Easter

St. Denio—11. 11. 11. 11.

Author unknown   Welsh hymn melody

1 We wel-come glad Easter when Je-sus a - rose And won a great vic - to - ry o - ver His foes. Then raise your glad voic-es, ye chil-dren, and sing, Bring sweet Easter prais-es to Je-sus, our King.

2
And tell how three Marys came early
    that day
And there at the tomb found the
    stone rolled away.
Then raise your glad voices, ye
    children, and sing,
Bring sweet Easter praises to Jesus,
    our King.

3
And sing of the angel who said: "Do
    not fear!
Your Savior is ris'n again; He is
    not here."
Then raise your glad voices, ye
    children, and sing,
Bring sweet Easter praises to Jesus,
    our King.

4
So think of the promise which Jesus
    did give,
That he who believes in Him also
    shall live.
Then raise your glad voices, ye
    children, and sing,
Bring sweet Easter praises to Jesus,
    our King.

We Will Carol Joyfully

Easter Carol—7. 7. 7. 7. 8. 7.

Author unknown

Composer unknown

1 We will car-ol joy-ful-ly On this ho-ly, hap-py day;

To our ris-en Lord and King Praise and wor-ship we will bring.

Car-ol, car-ol, car-ol, car-ol To our ris-en Lord and King.

2
We will carol joyfully
    As with happy songs we bring
Praise from ev'ry heart and voice
To our risen Lord and King.
    Carol, carol, etc.

3
We will carol joyfully
    While our love and thanks we give
To our risen Lord, and King,
Him who died that we might live.
    Carol, carol, etc.

4
We will carol joyfully
    And to Him our off'rings bring,
Grateful hearts, with love and praise,
To our risen Lord and King.
    Carol, carol, etc.

Come, Ye Children, Sing to Jesus

Lord, Revive Us —8.7.8.7. with Refrain

F. Smith

Early American melody

Come, ye chil-dren, sing to Je-sus On this hap-py East-er Day,
Christ, our Sav-ior, now is ris-en, Let His lit-tle chil-dren say.

All the bells are glad-ly ring-ing, All the flowers are gai-ly spring-ing,

All the birds with joy are sing-ing; Come, ye chil-dren, praise and pray.

Jesus High in Glory

Eudoxia—6. 5. 6. 5.

Author unknown

Sabine Baring-Gould, 1865

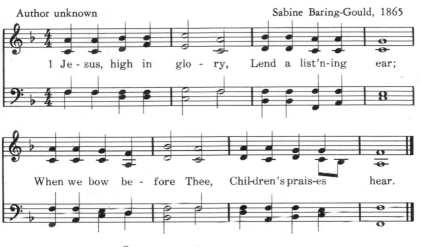

1 Je-sus, high in glo-ry, Lend a list'n-ing ear;

When we bow be-fore Thee, Chil-dren's prais-es hear.

2
Though Thou art so holy,
  Heav'n's almighty King,
Thou wilt stoop to listen
  When Thy praise we sing.

3
We are little children,
  Weak and apt to stray;
Savior, guide and keep us
  In the heav'nly way.

4
Save us, Lord, from sinning;
  Watch us day by day;
Help us now to love Thee;
  Take our sins away.

5
Then when Thou dost call us
  To our heav'nly home,
We shall gladly answer:
  Savior, Lord, we come.

Resources
for
Worship

ORDERS *of* WORSHIP

The CHRISTIAN CREEDS

PSALMS

OTHER SCRIPTURE SELECTIONS

The CATECHISM

PRAYERS

ORDERS *of* WORSHIP

I. General

THE INVOCATION

The leader shall say:

In the name of the Father and of the Son and of the Holy Ghost. Amen.

THE OPENING HYMN

The opening hymn shall be one of adoration, or it may be a morning hymn, or a hymn suitable to the season. All shall stand

THE SENTENCES

V. The Lord is nigh unto all them that call upon Him:

R. To all that call upon Him in truth.

V. O Lord, open Thou my lips:

R. And my mouth shall show forth Thy praise.

3

THE GLORIA PATRI

Glo-ry be to the Fa-ther and to the Son and to the Ho-ly Ghost, As it was in the be-gin-ning, is now, and ev-er shall be, world with-out end. A-men, A-men.

THE PRAYER

> *A selection from the prayers, pages 70—73, may be read by the leader or by the group*

THE SCRIPTURE READING

> *A Psalm or other selection of Scripture, pages 30—57, may be read responsively or in unison*

THE CATECHISM

> *A part of the Catechism, pages 58—69, may be read or recited*

THE OFFERING

THE HYMN STUDY

THE BIBLE INSTRUCTION FOR THE DAY

THE CLOSING HYMN

All shall stand

THE LESSON PRAYER

THE BENEDICTION

The grace of our Lord Jesus Christ, the love of God, and the communion of the Holy Spirit be with you all. Amen.

SILENT PRAYER

II. Praise and Thanksgiving

THE CALL TO WORSHIP

The leader shall say:

Oh, come, let us worship the Lord, for He is our Maker. Enter into His gates with thanksgiving, and into His courts with praise.

THE OPENING HYMN

THE SENTENCES

V. Bless the Lord, O my soul:

R. And all that is within me, bless His holy name.

V. Bless the Lord, O my soul:

R. And forget not all His benefits.

V. Who forgiveth all thine iniquities:

R. Who healeth all thy diseases.

V. Who redeemeth thy life from destruction:

R. Who crowneth thee with loving-kindness and tender mercies;

V. Who satisfieth thy mouth with good things:

R. So that thy youth is renewed like the eagle's.

5

THE GLORIA PATRI

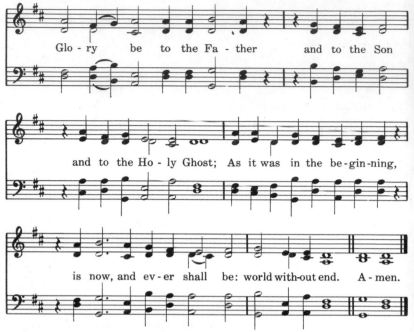

Glo - ry be to the Fa - ther and to the Son and to the Ho - ly Ghost; As it was in the be-gin-ning, is now, and ev - er shall be: world with-out end. A - men.

THE MORNING PRAYER

THE SCRIPTURE READING

THE PRAYER OF THANKSGIVING

THE OFFERING

THE HYMN STUDY

THE BIBLE INSTRUCTION FOR THE DAY

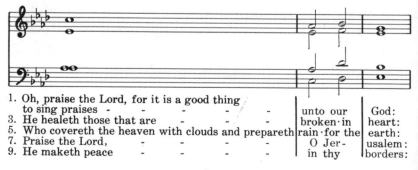

1. Oh, praise the Lord, for it is a good thing						
to sing praises -	-	-	-	-	unto our	God:
3. He healeth those that are	-	-	-	-	broken·in	heart:
5. Who covereth the heaven with clouds and prepareth					rain·for the	earth:
7. Praise the Lord,	-	-	-	-	O Jer-	usalem:
9. He maketh peace	-	-	-	-	in thy	borders:

6

1. yea, a joyful and pleasant thing it - | is to be | thank - | ful.
3. and giveth medicine to - - | heal their | sick- | ness.
5. and maketh the grass to grow upon the | herb for the | use of | men.
   mountains, and - - - - |
7. praise thy - - - - | God, O | Si - | on.
9. and filleth thee - - - - | with the | flour of | wheat.

2. The Lord doth build - - - - | up Jer- | usalem:
4. Oh, sing unto the Lord with thanks - - | giv - | ing:
6. Who giveth fodder - - - - | unto·the | cattle:
8. For He hath made fast the - - - | bars of·thy | gates:
10. Glory be to the Father and to the Son and to the | Holy | Ghost:

2. and gather together the - - - | outcasts of | Is-ra- | el.
4. sing praises upon the - - - | harp un- | to our | God.
6. and feedeth the young - - - | ravens ·that | call up on | Him.
8. and hath blessed thy - - - | children·with- | in | thee.
10. As it was in the beginning, is now,
    and ever shall be, - - - | world·without | end. A | men.

THE LESSON PRAYER

THE BENEDICAMUS

    V. Bless we the Lord:

    R. Thanks be to God.

SILENT PRAYER

III. Advent

The leader shall say:

The voice of one crying in the wilderness, Prepare ye the way of the Lord; make His paths straight.

THE OPENING HYMN

The opening hymn shall be a hymn suitable to the season

THE SENTENCES

V. Every valley shall be exalted, and every mountain and hill shall be made low:

R. And the crooked shall be made straight, and the rough places plain.

V. And the glory of the Lord shall be revealed, and all flesh shall see it together:

R. For the mouth of the Lord hath spoken it.

V. O Zion, that bringest good tidings, get thee up into the high mountain:

R. O Jerusalem, that bringest good tidings, lift up thy voice with strength.

V. Lift it up, be not afraid:

R. He shall gather the lambs with His arm, and carry them in His bosom.

THE GLORIA PATRI

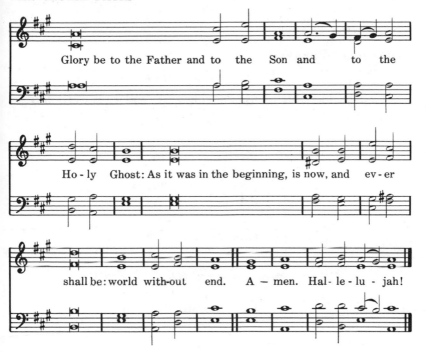

Glory be to the Father and to the Son and to the Ho-ly Ghost: As it was in the beginning, is now, and ev-er shall be: world with-out end. A — men. Hal-le-lu-jah!

THE PRAYER

An Advent prayer, page 79, may be read by the leader or by the group

THE SCRIPTURE READING

A Psalm or other selection of Scripture, pages 30—57, may be read responsively or in unison

THE CATECHISM

A part of the Catechism, pages 58—69, may be read or recited

THE OFFERING

THE HYMN STUDY

THE BIBLE INSTRUCTION FOR THE DAY

THE CLOSING HYMN

All shall stand

THE LESSON PRAYER

THE CLOSING PRAYER

To be said in unison

God be merciful to us, and bless us; and cause His face to shine upon us. Amen.

IV. Christmas

THE CALL TO WORSHIP

The leader shall say:

Unto us a Child is born, unto us a Son is given, and the government shall be upon His shoulder, and His name shall be called Wonderful, Counselor, the Mighty God, the Everlasting Father, the Prince of Peace.

THE OPENING HYMN

THE SENTENCES

V. The people that walked in darkness have seen a great light:

R. Unto them hath the light shined.

V. Oh, sing unto the Lord a new song:

R. Sing unto the Lord, all the earth.

V. Give unto the Lord the glory due unto His name:

R. Bring an offering, and come into His courts.

THE MAGNIFICAT

The Magnificat may either be sung or said

1 My	soul doth - - -	magni-	fy	the	Lord:
2 For	He - - -	hath	re-	gard-	ed:
3 For,	be- - - -	hold,	from	hence-	forth:
4 For	He that is mighty hath	done to	me	great	things:
5 And His	mercy is on - -	them	that	fear	Him:
6 He hath	showed - - -	strength	with	His	arm:
7 He hath	put down the -	mighty	from	their	seats:
8 He hath	filled the - - -	hungry	with	good	things:
9 He hath	holpen His servant Is-				
	rael in remembrance	of	His	mer -	cy:
Glo - ry	be to the Father -	and	to	the	Son:
As it	was in the beginning,				
	is now, and - -	ev-	er	shall	be:

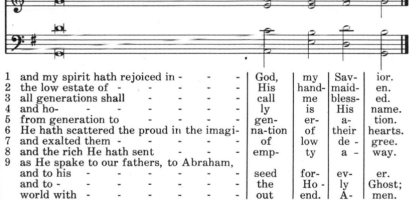

1 and my spirit hath rejoiced in - - -	God,	my	Sav-	ior.
2 the low estate of - - - -	His	hand-	maid-	en.
3 all generations shall - - - -	call	me	bless-	ed.
4 and ho- - - - - -	ly	is	His	name.
5 from generation to - - - -	gen-	er-	a-	tion.
6 He hath scattered the proud in the imagi-	na-tion	of	their	hearts.
7 and exalted them - - - -	of	low	de -	gree.
8 and the rich He hath sent - - -	emp-	ty	a -	way.
9 as He spake to our fathers, to Abraham,				
and to his - - - - - -	seed	for-	ev-	er.
and to - - - - - -	the	Ho -	ly	Ghost;
world with - - - - -	out	end.	A-	men.

THE PRAYER

The Christmas prayer, page 74, or some other seasonal prayer may be read by the leader or by the group

11

THE SCRIPTURE READING

An appropriate Scripture selection, pages 30—57,
may be read responsively or in unison

THE NICENE CREED

THE OFFERING

THE HYMN STUDY

THE BIBLE INSTRUCTION FOR THE DAY

THE CLOSING HYMN

THE LESSON PRAYER

THE CLOSING SENTENCE

Now unto the King eternal, immortal, invisible, the only wise God, be honor and glory forever and ever. Amen.

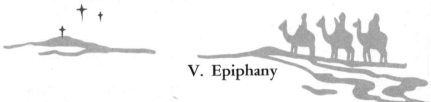

V. Epiphany

THE CALL TO WORSHIP

The leader shall say:

Make a joyful noise unto God, all ye lands: sing forth the honor of His name; make His praise glorious.

THE MORNING PRAYER

Luther's Morning Prayer appears on page 88

THE OPENING HYMN

THE SCRIPTURE READING

A Psalm or other selection of Scripture, pages
30—57, may be read by the leader or by the
group

THE CATECHISM

*A part of the Catechism, pages 58—69, may be
read or recited*

THE OFFERING

THE HYMN STUDY

THE PRAYER

*The Epiphany prayer, page 75, or a general prayer
may be read by the leader, by the group,
or by one of the pupils*

THE BIBLE INSTRUCTION FOR THE DAY

THE NUNC DIMITTIS

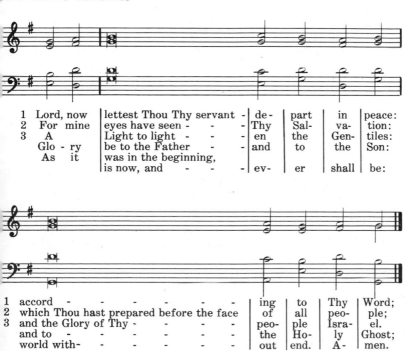

1 Lord, now | lettest Thou Thy servant - | de- | part | in | peace:
2 For mine | eyes have seen - - - | Thy | Sal- | va- | tion:
3 A | Light to light - - - | en | the | Gen- | tiles:
Glo - ry | be to the Father - - | and | to | the | Son:
As it | was in the beginning, | | | |
| is now, and - - - | ev- | er | shall | be:

1 accord - - - - - - | ing | to | Thy | Word;
2 which Thou hast prepared before the face | of | all | peo- | ple;
3 and the Glory of Thy - - - - | peo- | ple | Isra- | el.
and to - - - - - - | the | Ho- | ly | Ghost;
world with- - - - - - | out | end. | A- | men.

13

THE MIZPAH BLESSING

The Lord watch between me and thee when we are absent one from another. Amen.

VI. Pre-Lent

THE INVOCATION

The leader shall say:

The Lord is in His holy Temple: Let all the earth keep silence before Him.

THE OPENING HYMN

*The opening hymn shall be one of faith and trust
in the Redeemer*

THE SENTENCES

V. The blood of Jesus Christ, God's Son, cleanseth us from all sin:

R. Create in me a clean heart, O God.

14

V. He that believeth and is baptized shall be saved.
R. Grant us this salvation, O Lord.

THE SCRIPTURE READING

A Psalm or other selection of Scripture, pages 30—57, may be read responsively or in unison

THE LORD'S PRAYER

A reading of some other part of the Catechism may be substituted

THE OFFERING

THE HYMN STUDY

THE GENERAL PRAYER

A selection from the prayers, pages 70—73, may be read by the leader or by the group

THE BIBLE INSTRUCTION FOR THE DAY

THE CLOSING SENTENCES

All shall stand

V. The fear of the Lord is the beginning of wisdom:
R. A good understanding have all they that do His commandments.
V. Thy Word is a lamp unto my feet:
R. And a light unto my path.
V. O Lord, let Thy mercy be upon us:
R. As our trust is in Thee.

THE LESSON PRAYER

THE BENEDICTION

The leader shall say:

The Lord be with you and keep you. Amen.

15

VII. Lent

THE CALL TO WORSHIP

The leader shall say:

Christ became obedient unto death, even the death of the cross. Oh, come, let us worship Him!

THE HYMN

THE SENTENCES

V. If we say that we have no sin, we deceive ourselves, and the truth is not in us:

R. If we confess our sins, He is faithful and just to forgive us our sins and to cleanse us from all unrighteousness.

THE PRAYER

The Lenten prayer, page 75, or a selection from the prayers (pages 85—87) may be said by the leader or by the group

THE CATECHISM

A part of the Catechism, pages 58—69, may be read , or one of the Creeds, page 26, may be recited

THE OFFERING

THE HYMN STUDY

THE BIBLE INSTRUCTION FOR THE DAY

16

THE AGNUS DEI

O Christ, Thou Lamb of God, that tak-est a-way the sin of the world, have mer-cy up-on us. O Christ, Thou Lamb of God, that tak-est a-way the sin of the world, have mer-cy up-on us. O Christ, Thou Lamb of God, that tak-est a-way the sin of the world, grant us Thy peace. A - - men.

THE BENEDICTION

The grace of our Lord Jesus Christ be with you all. Amen.

17

VIII. Palm Sunday

THE CALL TO WORSHIP

Blessed is the king that cometh in the name of the Lord: Peace in heaven and glory in the highest.

THE OPENING HYMN

The hymn shall be a praise of the Redeemer

THE SCRIPTURE READING

To be read by the leader or by the group:

And when they drew near to Jerusalem, to Bethphage and Bethany, at the Mount of Olives, He sent two of His disciples and said to them: "Go into the village ahead of you, and immediately, as you enter it, you will find a colt tied, on which no one has ever sat; untie it, and bring it to Me. If anyone asks you: Why are you doing this? say: The Lord needs it, and he will send it here immediately." So the disciples did as He told them, and found a colt tied at the door out in the open street; and they untied it. And those who stood there said to them: "What are you doing, untying the colt?" And they told them what Jesus had said; and the owners let them go. And they brought the colt to Jesus and threw their garments on it; and He sat upon it. And many spread their garments on the road, and others spread leafy branches which they had cut from palm trees. And those who went before and those who followed shouted: "Hosanna! Blessed be He who comes in the name of the Lord! Hosanna in the highest!"

18

THE PRAYER·

The Palm Sunday prayer is on page 75

THE OFFERING

THE HYMN STUDY

THE BIBLE INSTRUCTION FOR THE DAY
All shall stand

THE LESSON PRAYER

THE CLOSING SENTENCES

> V. Let this mind be in you which was also in Christ Jesus:
>
> R. Who, being in the form of God, thought it not robbery to be equal with God;
>
> V. But made Himself of no reputation, and took upon Him the form of a servant, and was made in the likeness of men:
>
> R. And being found in fashion as a man, He humbled Himself, and became obedient unto death, even the death of the cross.
>
> V. Wherefore God also hath highly exalted Him and given Him a name which is above every name:
>
> R. That at the name of Jesus every knee should bow, of things in heaven, and things in earth, and things under the earth;

ALL: And that every tongue should confess that Jesus Christ is Lord, to the glory of God the Father.

19

IX. Easter

THE INVOCATION

In the name of our risen Lord and Savior. Amen.

THE OPENING HYMN

THE SENTENCES

V. This is the day which the Lord hath made:

R. We will rejoice and be glad in it.

V. He is risen!

R. The Lord is risen indeed. Alleluia!

V. Oh, sing unto the Lord a new song:

R. For He hath done marvelous things.

V. Our Lord Jesus said: I am the Resurrection and the Life; he that believeth in Me, though he were dead, yet shall he live:

R. And he that liveth and believeth in Me shall never die.

THE EASTER HYMN OF PRAISE

THE PRAYER

The Easter prayer is on page 76

The Easter prayer is on page 76

THE NICENE CREED

The Creeds are on page 26

The Creeds are on page 26

THE OFFERING

THE BIBLE INSTRUCTION FOR THE DAY

THE CLOSING HYMN

THE LESSON PRAYER

THE DOXOLOGY

X. Pentecost

The leader may say:

Holy Spirit, hear us
On this sacred day;
Come to us with blessing,
Come with us to stay.

THE OPENING HYMN

THE SENTENCES

V. As many as are led by the Spirit of God:

R. They are the sons of God.

V. Our Lord Jesus said: The Comforter, who is the Holy Spirit, whom the Father will send in My name:

R. He shall teach you all things and bring all things to your remembrance.

V. He shall testify of Me:

R. He will guide you into all truth. He shall glorify Me.

V. Come, Holy Spirit, and fill the hearts of Thy faithful people:

R. And kindle in them the fire of Thy love.

THE SCRIPTURE READING

RESPONSIVE PRAYER

The following or some other suitable prayer may be used

Leader: Let us pray for the gift of the Holy Spirit, that He may ever open our eyes to the truth that Jesus is our living Lord and Savior and that we may ever walk in the light of that truth.

Response: Lord God, grant us Thy Holy Spirit, through Jesus Christ, Thy Son, our Lord.

Leader: Let us ask God to send His Holy Spirit into the hearts of all men, that the whole world may be brought out of the darkness of sin into the light which only Christ can give, that they, too, may receive forgiveness of sins and life everlasting.

Response: O God, send forth Thy Spirit, and turn many from darkness to light.

Leader: Let us pray to God for the blessings of His Spirit: The Spirit of wisdom and knowledge, of grace and prayer, of power and strength, of sanctification and the fear of God.

Response: Grant us the blessings of Thy Spirit, O God.

Leader: Let us also ask God to produce in us the fruit of the Spirit. The fruit of the Spirit is love, joy, peace, long-suffering, gentleness, goodness, faith, meekness, temperance.

Response: If we live in the Spirit, let us also walk in the Spirit.

THE CATECHISM

THE PRAYER

A prayer for the Holy Spirit is on page 76

THE OFFERING

THE HYMN STUDY

22

THE BIBLE INSTRUCTION FOR THE DAY

THE CLOSING HYMN

All shall stand

THE LESSON PRAYER

THE BENEDICTION

The grace of the Lord Jesus Christ and the love of God and the communion of the Holy Spirit be with you all. Amen.

XI. Trinity Season

THE OPENING HYMN

THE CONFESSION OF SIN

The children may kneel or stand as they say the General Confession, p. 90, or the following in unison

Remember, O Lord, Thy tender mercies and Thy loving-kindnesses; for they have been ever of old. Remember not the sins of my youth nor my transgressions. According to Thy mercy remember Thou me for Thy goodness' sake, O Lord.

THE KYRIE

V. O God the Father in heaven:
R. Have mercy upon us!
V. O God the Son, Redeemer of the world:
R. Have mercy upon us!
V. O God the Holy Spirit, true Comforter:
R. Have mercy upon us!

THE ASSURANCE OF FORGIVENESS

The leader shall say the following:

If we say that we have no sin, we deceive ourselves, and the truth is not in us. But if we confess our sins, God is faithful and just to forgive us our sins and to cleanse us from all unrighteousness. He forgives and cleanses us for the sake of our Lord Jesus, who died for us in order to save us.

THE GLORIA IN EXCELSIS

V. Glory to God in the highest:

R. And on earth peace, good will toward men.

THE HYMN STUDY OR CHOIR

THE GENERAL PRAYER

A selection from the prayers, pages 70—73, may be read by the leader or by the group

THE OFFERING

THE BIBLE INSTRUCTION FOR THE DAY

THE LESSON PRAYER

THE CLOSING HYMN

THE BENEDICTION

May the grace of Christ, our Savior,
And the Father's boundless love,
With the Holy Spirit's favor,
Rest upon us from above. Amen.

24

XII. A Brief Order for Home Devotions

(Parents should feel free to vary this suggested pattern and will do well to enlist their children's participation as much as possible.)

1. All sing a hymn.
2. Scripture reading by the father.
3. The reading from a book of meditations by an older child.
4. The prayer by the father or the mother.
5. A simple hymn for the small child present — or a doxology.
6. The reciting of a part of the Catechism in unison; e. g., the Ten Commandments, the Creed, the Lord's Prayer, and the Morning and Evening Prayers.

I. The Apostles' Creed

I believe in God the Father Almighty, Maker of heaven and earth.

And in Jesus Christ, His only Son, our Lord; Who was conceived by the Holy Ghost, Born of the Virgin Mary; Suffered under Pontius Pilate, Was crucified, dead, and buried; He descended into hell; The third day He rose again from the dead; He ascended into heaven, And sitteth on the right hand of God the Father Almighty; From thence He shall come to judge the quick and the dead.

I believe in the Holy Ghost; The holy Christian Church, the communion of saints; The forgiveness of sins; The resurrection of the body; And the life everlasting. Amen.

II. The Nicene Creed

I believe in one God, the Father Almighty, Maker of heaven and earth and of all things visible and invisible.

And in one Lord Jesus Christ, the only-begotten Son of God, begotten of His Father before all worlds, God of God, Light of Light, Very God of Very God, Begotten, not made, Being of one substance with the Father, By whom all things were made; Who for us men and for our salvation came down from heaven And was incarnate by the Holy Ghost of the Virgin Mary And was made man; And was crucified also for us under Pontius Pilate.

He suffered and was buried; And the third day He rose again according to the Scriptures; And ascended into heaven, And sitteth on the right hand of the Father; And He shall come again with glory to judge both the quick and the dead; Whose kingdom shall have no end.

And I believe in the Holy Ghost, The Lord and Giver of Life, Who proceedeth from the Father and the Son, Who with the Father and the Son together is worshiped and glorified, Who spake by the Prophets. And I believe one holy Christian and Apostolic Church. I acknowledge one Baptism for the remission of sins, And I look for the resurrection of the dead; And the life of the world to come. Amen.

III. The Athanasian Creed

Whosoever will be saved, before all things it is necessary that he hold the catholic * faith.

Which faith except everyone do keep whole and undefiled, without doubt he shall perish everlastingly.

And the catholic faith is this, that we worship one God in Trinity and Trinity in Unity,

Neither confounding the Persons nor dividing the Substance.

For there is one Person of the Father, another of the Son, and another of the Holy Ghost.

But the Godhead of the Father, of the Son, and of the Holy Ghost is all one: the glory equal, the majesty coeternal.

Such as the Father is, such is the Son, and such is the Holy Ghost.

The Father uncreate, the Son uncreate, and the Holy Ghost uncreate.

The Father incomprehensible, the Son incomprehensible, and the Holy Ghost incomprehensible.

The Father eternal, the Son eternal, and the Holy Ghost eternal.

---

* Which means the universal, Christian faith.

And yet .they are not three Eternals, but one Eternal,

As there are not three Uncreated nor three Incomprehensibles, but one Uncreated and one Incomprehensible.

So likewise the Father is almighty, the Son almighty, and the Holy Ghost almighty.

And yet they are not three Almighties, but one Almighty.

So the Father is God, the Son is God, and the Holy Ghost is God.

And yet they are not three Gods, but one God.

So likewise the Father is Lord, the Son is Lord, and the Holy Ghost is Lord.

And yet not three Lords, but one Lord.

For like as we are compelled by the Christian verity to acknowledge every Person by Himself to be God and Lord,

So are we forbidden by the catholic religion to say, There be three Gods or three Lords.

The Father is made of none, neither created nor begotten.

The Son is of the Father alone, not made nor created, but begotten.

The Holy Ghost is of the Father and of the Son, neither made nor created nor begotten, but proceeding.

So there is one Father, not three Fathers; one Son, not three Sons; one Holy Ghost, not three Holy Ghosts.

And in this Trinity none is before or after other; none is greater or less than another;

But the whole three Persons are coeternal together and coequal, so that in all things, as is aforesaid, the Unity in Trinity and the Trinity in Unity is to be worshiped.

He, therefore, that will be saved must thus think of the Trinity.

Furthermore, it is necessary to everlasting salvation that he also believe faithfully the incarnation of our Lord Jesus Christ.

For the right faith is that we believe and confess that our Lord Jesus Christ, the Son of God, is God and Man;

God of the Substance of the Father, begotten before the world; and Man of the substance of His mother, born in the world;

Perfect God and perfect Man, of a reasonable soul and human flesh subsisting.

Equal to the Father as touching His Godhead and inferior to the Father as touching His manhood;

Who, although He be God and Man, yet He is not two, but one Christ;

One, not by conversion of the Godhead into flesh, but by taking the manhood into God;

One altogether; not by confusion of Substance, but by unity of Person.

For as the reasonable soul and flesh is one man, so God and Man is one Christ;

Who suffered for our salvation; descended into hell; rose again the third day from the dead;

He ascended into heaven; He sitteth on the right hand of the Father, God Almighty; from whence He shall come to judge the quick and the dead.

At whose coming all men shall rise again with their bodies and shall give an account of their own works.

And they that have done good shall go into life everlasting; and they that have done evil, into everlasting fire.

This is the catholic faith; which except a man believe faithfully and firmly, he cannot be saved.

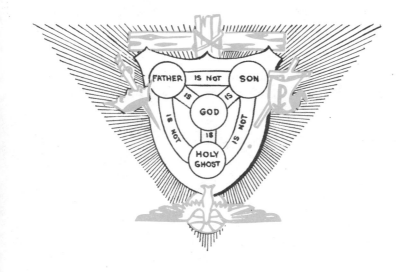

PSALMS *and* OTHER SCRIPTURE SELECTIONS

PSALM 1

1. Blessed is the man that walketh not in the counsel of the ungodly, nor standeth in the way of sinners: nor sitteth in the seat of the scornful.

2. But his delight is in the Law of the Lord: and in His Law doth he meditate day and night.

3. And he shall be like a tree planted by the rivers of water; that bringeth forth his fruit in his season; his leaf also shall not wither: and whatsoever he doeth shall prosper.

4. The ungodly are not so: but are like the chaff which the wind driveth away.

5. Therefore the ungodly shall not stand in the judgment: nor sinners in the congregation of the righteous.

6. For the Lord knoweth the way of the righteous: but the way of the ungodly shall perish.

To be said or sung by all:

Glory be to the Father and to the Son and to the Holy Ghost; As it was in the beginning, is now, and ever shall be: world without end. Amen.

PSALM 8

1. O Lord, our Lord, how excellent is Thy name in all the earth: Who hast set Thy glory above the heavens!

2. Out of the mouth of babes and sucklings hast Thou ordained strength because of Thine enemies: that Thou mightest still the enemy and the avenger.

30

3. When I consider Thy heavens, the work of Thy fingers: the moon and the stars, which Thou hast ordained;

4. What is man, that Thou art mindful of him: and the Son of Man, that Thou visitest Him?

5. For Thou hast made Him a little lower than the angels: and hast crowned Him with glory and honor.

6. Thou madest Him to have dominion over the works of Thy hands: Thou hast put all things under His feet.

7. All sheep and oxen, yea, and the beast of the field;

8. The fowl of the air, and the fish of the sea, and whatsoever passeth through the paths of the seas.

9. O Lord, our Lord, how excellent is Thy name in all the earth!

Glory be to the Father, etc.

PSALM 14

1. The fool hath said in his heart, There is no God: They are corrupt; they have done abominable works; there is none that doeth good.

2. The Lord looked down from heaven upon the children of men: to see if there were any that did understand and seek God.

3. They are all gone aside, they are all together become filthy: there is none that doeth good, no, not one.

4. Have all the workers of iniquity no knowledge? who eat up My people as they eat bread and call not upon the Lord.

5. There were they in great fear: for God is in the generation of the righteous.

6. Ye have shamed the counsel of the poor: because the Lord is his Refuge.

7. Oh, that the salvation of Israel were come out of Zion! When the Lord bringeth back the captivity of His people: Jacob shall rejoice, and Israel shall be glad.

Glory be to the Father, etc.

1. The heavens declare the glory of God: and the firmament showeth His handiwork.

2. Day unto day uttereth speech: and night unto night showeth knowledge.

3. There is no speech nor language: where their voice is not heard.

4. Their line is gone out through all the earth: and their words to the end of the world.

5. In them hath He set a tabernacle for the sun: which is as a bridegroom coming out of his chamber and rejoiceth as a strong man to run a race.

6. His going forth is from the end of the heaven and his circuit unto the ends of it: and there is nothing hid from the heat thereof.

7. The Law of the Lord is perfect, converting the soul: the testimony of the Lord is sure, making wise the simple.

8. The statutes of the Lord are right, rejoicing the heart: the commandment of the Lord is pure, enlightening the eyes.

9. The fear of the Lord is clean, enduring forever: the judgments of the Lord are true and righteous altogether.

10. More to be desired are they than gold, yea, than much fine gold: sweeter also than honey and the honeycomb.

11. Moreover, by them is Thy servant warned: and in keeping of them there is great reward.

12. Who can understand his errors?: Cleanse Thou me from secret faults.

13. Keep back Thy servant also from presumptuous sins; let them not have dominion over me: then shall I be upright, and I shall be innocent from the great transgression.

14. Let the words of my mouth and the meditation of my heart be acceptable in Thy sight: O Lord, my Strength and my Redeemer.

Glory be to the Father, etc.

PSALM 23

1. The Lord is my Shepherd: I shall not want.

2. He maketh me to lie down in green pastures: He leadeth me beside the still waters.

3. He restoreth my soul: He leadeth me in the paths of righteousness for His name's sake.

4. Yea, though I walk through the valley of the shadow of death, I will fear no evil: for Thou art with me; Thy rod and Thy staff, they comfort me.

5. Thou preparest a table before me in the presence of mine enemies: Thou anointest my head with oil; my cup runneth over.

6. Surely goodness and mercy shall follow me all the days of my life: and I will dwell in the house of the Lord forever.

Glory be to the Father, etc.

PSALM 24

1. The earth is the Lord's and the fulness thereof: the world and they that dwell therein.

2. For He hath founded it upon the seas: and established it upon the floods.

3. Who shall ascend into the hill of the Lord: or who shall stand in His Holy Place?

4. He that hath clean hands and a pure heart: who hath not lifted up his soul unto vanity nor sworn deceitfully.

33

5. He shall receive the blessing from the Lord: and righteousness from the God of his salvation.

    6. This is the generation of them that seek Him: that seek thy face, O Jacob.

7. Lift up your heads, O ye gates; and be ye lift up, ye everlasting doors: and the King of Glory shall come in.

    8. Who is this King of Glory?: The Lord strong and mighty, the Lord mighty in battle.

9. Lift up your heads, O ye gates; even lift them up, ye everlasting doors: and the King of Glory shall come in.

    10. Who is this King of Glory?: The Lord of Hosts, He is the King of Glory.

Glory be to the Father, etc.

PSALM 25

1. Unto Thee, O Lord: do I lift up my soul.

    2. O my God, I trust in Thee: let me not be ashamed, let not mine enemies triumph over me.

3. Yea, let none that wait upon Thee be ashamed: let them be ashamed which transgress without cause.

    4. Show me Thy ways, O Lord: teach me Thy paths.

5. Lead me in Thy truth and teach me: for Thou art the God of my salvation; on Thee do I wait all the day.

    6. Remember, O Lord, Thy tender mercies and Thy loving-kindnesses: for they have been ever of old.

7. Remember not the sins of my youth nor my transgressions: according to Thy mercy remember Thou me for Thy goodness' sake, O Lord.

    8. Good and upright is the Lord: therefore will He teach sinners in the way.

9. The meek will He guide in judgment: and the meek will He teach His way.

    10. All the paths of the Lord are mercy and truth: unto such as keep His covenant and His testimonies.

34

1. God is our Refuge and Strength: a very present Help in trouble.

2. Therefore will not we fear though the earth be removed: and though the mountains be carried into the midst of the sea;

3. Though the waters thereof roar and be troubled: though the mountains shake with the swelling thereof.

4. There is a river the streams whereof shall make glad the city of God: the holy place of the tabernacles of the Most High.

5. God is in the midst of her; she shall not be moved: God shall help her, and that right early.

6. The heathen raged, the kingdoms were moved: He uttered His voice, the earth melted.

7. The Lord of Hosts is with us: the God of Jacob is our Refuge.

8. Come, behold the works of the Lord: what desolations He hath made in the earth.

9. He maketh wars to cease unto the end of the earth: He breaketh the bow and cutteth the spear in sunder; He burneth the chariot in the fire.

10. Be still and know that I am God: I will be exalted among the heathen, I will be exalted in the earth.

11. The Lord of Hosts is with us: the God of Jacob is our Refuge.

Glory be to the Father, etc.

PSALM 51

1. Have mercy upon me, O God, according to Thy loving-kindness: according unto the multitude of Thy tender mercies blot out my transgressions.

2. Wash me thoroughly from mine iniquity: and cleanse me from my sin.

3. For I acknowledge my transgressions: and my sin is ever before me.

4. *Against Thee, Thee only, have I sinned and done this evil in Thy sight: that Thou mightest be justified when Thou speakest and be clear when Thou judgest.*

5. Behold, I was shapen in iniquity: and in sin did my mother conceive me.

6. *Behold, Thou desirest truth in the inward parts: and in the hidden part Thou shalt make me to know wisdom.*

7. Purge me with hyssop, and I shall be clean: wash me, and I shall be whiter than snow.

8. *Make me to hear joy and gladness: that the bones which Thou hast broken may rejoice.*

9. Hide Thy face from my sins: and blot out all mine iniquities.

10. *Create in me a clean heart, O God: and renew a right spirit within me.*

11. Cast me not away from Thy presence: and take not Thy Holy Spirit from me.

12. *Restore unto me the joy of Thy salvation: and uphold me with Thy free Spirit.*

13. Then will I teach transgressors Thy ways: and sinners shall be converted unto Thee.

14. *O Lord, open Thou my lips: and my mouth shall show forth Thy praise.*

15. For Thou desirest not sacrifice, else would I give it: Thou delightest not in burnt offering.

16. *The sacrifices of God are a broken spirit: a broken and a contrite heart, O God, Thou wilt not despise.*

PSALM 67

1. God be merciful unto us and bless us: and cause His face to shine upon us.

2. *That Thy way may be known upon earth: Thy saving health among all nations.*

3. Let the people praise Thee, O God: let all the people praise Thee.

4. Oh, let the nations be glad and sing for joy: for Thou shalt judge the people righteously and govern the nations upon earth.

5. Let the people praise Thee, O God: let all the people praise Thee.

6. Then shall the earth yield her increase: and God, even our own God, shall bless us.

7. God shall bless us: and all the ends of the earth shall fear Him.

Glory be to the Father, etc.

PSALM 84

1. How amiable arc Thy tabernacles: O Lord of Hosts!

2. My soul longeth, yea, even fainteth, for the courts of the Lord: my heart and my flesh crieth out for the living God.

3. Yea, the sparrow hath found an house: and the swallow a nest for herself where she may lay her young, even Thine altars, O Lord of Hosts, my King and my God.

4. Blessed are they that dwell in Thy house: they will be still praising Thee.

5. Blessed is the man whose strength is in Thee: in whose heart are the ways of them;

6. Who, passing through the Valley of Baca, make it a well: the rain also filleth the pools.

7. They go from strength to strength: every one of them in Zion appeareth before God.

8. *O Lord God of Hosts, hear my prayer: give ear, O God of Jacob.*

9. Behold, O God, our Shield: and look upon the face of Thine anointed.

10. *For a day in Thy courts is better than a thousand: I had rather be a doorkeeper in the house of my God than to dwell in the tents of wickedness.*

11. For the Lord God is a Sun and Shield; the Lord will give grace and glory: no good thing will He withhold from them that walk uprightly.

12. *O Lord of Hosts: blessed is the man that trusteth in Thee.*

Glory be to the Father, etc.

PSALM 90

1. Lord, Thou hast been our dwelling place: in all generations.

2. *Before the mountains were brought forth or ever Thou hadst formed the earth and the world: even from everlasting to everlasting, Thou art God.*

3. Thou turnest man to destruction: and sayest, Return, ye children of men.

4. *For a thousand years in Thy sight are but as yesterday when it is past: and as a watch in the night.*

5. Thou carriest them away as with a flood; they are as a sleep: in the morning they are like grass which groweth up.

6. *In the morning it flourisheth and groweth up: in the evening it is cut down and withereth.*

7. For we are consumed by Thine anger: and by Thy wrath are we troubled.

8. *Thou hast set our iniquities before Thee: our secret sins in the light of Thy countenance.*

9. For all our days are passed away in Thy wrath: we spend our years as a tale that is told.

10. The days of our years are threescore years and ten; and if by reason of strength they be fourscore years: yet is their strength labor and sorrow; for it is soon cut off, and we fly away.

11. Who knoweth the power of Thine anger?: Even according to Thy fear, so is Thy wrath.

12. So teach us to number our days: that we may apply our hearts unto wisdom.

13. Return, O Lord, how long?: And let it repent Thee concerning Thy servants.

14. Oh, satisfy us early with Thy mercy: that we may rejoice and be glad in our days.

15. Make us glad according to the days wherein Thou hast afflicted us: and the years wherein we have seen evil.

16. Let Thy work appear unto Thy servants: and Thy glory unto their children.

17. And let the beauty of the Lord, our God, be upon us: and establish Thou the work of our hands upon us; yea, the work of our hands, establish Thou it.

Glory be to the Father, etc.

PSALM 91

1. He that dwelleth in the secret place of the Most High: shall abide under the shadow of the Almighty.

2. I will say of the Lord, He is my Refuge and my Fortress: my God; in Him will I trust.

3. Surely He shall deliver thee from the snare of the fowler: and from the noisome pestilence.

4. He shall cover thee with His feathers, and under His wings shalt thou trust: His truth shall be thy shield and buckler.

5. Thou shalt not be afraid for the terror by night: nor for the arrow that flieth by day;

6. *Nor for the pestilence that walketh in darkness: nor for the destruction that wasteth at noonday.*

7. A thousand shall fall at thy side and ten thousand at thy right hand: but it shall not come nigh thee.

8. *Only with thine eyes shalt thou behold: and see the reward of the wicked.*

9. Because thou hast made the Lord, which is my Refuge: even the Most High, thy habitation,

10. *There shall no evil befall thee: neither shall any plague come nigh thy dwelling.*

11. For He shall give His angels charge over thee: to keep thee in all thy ways.

12. *They shall bear thee up in their hands: lest thou dash thy foot against a stone.*

13. Thou shalt tread upon the lion and adder: the young lion and the dragon shalt thou trample under feet.

14. *Because he hath set his love upon Me, therefore will I deliver him: I will set him on high because he hath known My name.*

15. He shall call upon Me, and I will answer him: I will be with him in trouble; I will deliver him and honor him.

16. *With long life will I satisfy him: and show him My salvation.*

Glory be to the Father, etc.

PSALM 96

1. Oh, sing unto the Lord a new song: sing unto the Lord all the earth.

2. *Sing unto the Lord, bless His name: show forth His salvation from day to day.*

3. Declare His glory among the heathen: His wonders among all people.

4. *For the Lord is great and greatly to be praised: He is to be feared above all gods.*

40

5. For all the gods of the nations are idols: but the Lord made the heavens.

6. Honor and majesty are before Him: strength and beauty are in His Sanctuary.

7. Give unto the Lord, O ye kindreds of the people: give unto the Lord glory and strength.

8. Give unto the Lord the glory due unto His name: bring an offering and come into His courts.

9. Oh, worship the Lord in the beauty of holiness: fear before Him, all the earth.

10. Say among the heathen that the Lord reigneth; the world also shall be established that it shall not be moved: He shall judge the people righteously.

11. Let the heavens rejoice, and let the earth be glad: let the sea roar and the fulness thereof.

12. Let the field be joyful, and all that is therein: then shall all the trees of the wood rejoice

13. Before the Lord; for He cometh, for He cometh to judge the earth: He shall judge the world with righteousness and the people with His truth.

Glory be to the Father, etc.

PSALM 100

1. Make a joyful noise unto the Lord: all ye lands.

2. Serve the Lord with gladness: come before His presence with singing.

3. Know ye that the Lord He is God: it is He that hath made us and not we ourselves; we are His people and the sheep of His pasture.

4. Enter into His gates with thanksgiving, and into His courts with praise: be thankful unto Him, and bless His name.

5. For the Lord is good; His mercy is everlasting: and His truth endureth to all generations.

Glory be to the Father, etc.

PSALM 103

1. Bless the Lord, O my soul: and all that is within me, bless His holy name.

2. Bless the Lord, O my soul: and forget not all His benefits;

3. Who forgiveth all thine iniquities: who healeth all thy diseases;

4. Who redeemeth thy life from destruction: who crowneth thee with loving-kindness and tender mercies;

5. Who satisfieth thy mouth with good things: so that thy youth is renewed like the eagle's.

6. The Lord executeth righteousness and judgment: for all that are oppressed.

7. He made known His way unto Moses: His acts unto the children of Israel.

8. The Lord is merciful and gracious: slow to anger and plenteous in mercy.

9. He will not always chide: neither will He keep His anger forever.

10. He hath not dealt with us after our sins: nor rewarded us according to our iniquities.

11. For as the heaven is high above the earth: so great is His mercy toward them that fear Him.

12. As far as the east is from the west: so far hath He removed our transgressions from us.

13. Like as a father pitieth his children: so the Lord pitieth them that fear Him.

14. For He knoweth our frame: He remembereth that we are dust.

15. As for man, his days are as grass: as a flower of the field, so he flourisheth.

16. *For the wind passeth over it, and it is gone: and the place thereof shall know it no more.*

17. But the mercy of the Lord is from everlasting to everlasting upon them that fear Him: and His righteousness unto children's children,

18. *To such as Keep His covenant: and to those that remember His commandments to do them.*

19. The Lord hath prepared His throne in the heavens: and His kingdom ruleth over all.

20. *Bless the Lord, ye His angels, that excel in strength: that do His commandments, hearkening unto the voice of His word.*

21. Bless ye the Lord, all ye His hosts: ye ministers of His that do His pleasure.

22. *Bless the Lord, all His works, in all places of His dominion: Bless the Lord, O my soul.*

Glory be to the Father, etc.

PSALM 119 — SECTION A

1. Blessed are the undefiled in the way: who walk in the Law of the Lord.

2. *Blessed are they that keep His testimonies: and that seek Him with the whole heart.*

3. They also do no iniquity: they walk in His ways.

4. *Thou hast commanded us: to keep Thy precepts diligently.*

5. Oh, that my ways were directed: to keep Thy statutes!

6. *Then shall I not be ashamed: when I have respect unto all Thy commandments.*

43

7. I will praise Thee with uprightness of heart: when I shall have learned Thy righteous judgments.

8. *I will keep Thy statutes: Oh, forsake me not utterly!*

Glory be to the Father, etc.

PSALM 119 — SECTION B

1. Wherewithal shall a young man cleanse his way?: By taking heed thereto according to Thy Word.

2. *With my whole heart have I sought Thee: Oh, let me not wander from Thy commandments!*

3. Thy Word have I hid in mine heart: that I might not sin against Thee.

4. *Blessed art Thou, O Lord: teach me Thy statutes.*

5. With my lips have I declared: all the judgments of Thy mouth.

6. *I have rejoiced in the way of Thy testimonies: as much as in all riches.*

7. I will meditate in Thy precepts: and have respect unto Thy ways.

8. *I will delight myself in Thy statutes: I will not forget Thy Word.*

Glory be to the Father, etc.

PSALM 119 — SECTION C

1. Oh, how love I Thy Law!: It is my meditation all the day.

2. *Thou through Thy commandments hast made me wiser than mine enemies: for they are ever with me.*

3. I have more understanding than all my teachers: for Thy testimonies are my meditation.

4. *I understand more than the ancients: because I keep Thy precepts.*

44

5. I have refrained my feet from every evil way: that I might keep Thy Word.

6. *I have not departed from Thy judgments: for Thou hast taught me.*

7. How sweet are Thy words unto my taste!: yea, sweeter than honey to my mouth.

8. *Through Thy precepts I get understanding: therefore I hate every false way.*

Glory be to the Father, etc.

PSALM 121

1. I will lift up mine eyes unto the hills: from whence cometh my help.

2. *My help cometh from the Lord: which made heaven and earth.*

3. He will not suffer thy foot to be moved: He that keepeth thee will not slumber.

4. *Behold, He that keepeth Israel: shall neither slumber nor sleep.*

5. The Lord is thy Keeper: the Lord is thy Shade upon thy right hand.

6. *The sun shall not smite thee by day: nor the moon by night.*

7. The Lord shall preserve thee from all evil: He shall preserve thy soul.

8. *The Lord shall preserve thy going out and thy coming in: from this time forth and even forevermore.*

Glory be to the Father, etc.

PSALM 130

1. Out of the depths: have I cried unto Thee, O Lord.

2. *Lord, hear my voice: let Thine ears be attentive to the voice of my supplications.*

3. If Thou, Lord, shouldest mark iniquities: O Lord, who shall stand?

4. But there is forgiveness with Thee: that Thou mayest be feared.

5. I wait for the Lord, my soul doth wait: and in His Word do I hope.

6. My soul waiteth for the Lord more than they that watch for the morning: I say, more than they that watch for the morning.

7. Let Israel hope in the Lord: for with the Lord there is mercy, and with Him is plenteous redemption.

8. And He shall redeem Israel from all his iniquities.

Glory be to the Father, etc.

PSALM 145

1. I will extol Thee, my God, O King: and I will bless Thy name forever and ever.

2. Every day will I bless Thee: and I will praise Thy name forever and ever.

3. Great is the Lord and greatly to be praised: and His greatness is unsearchable.

4. One generation shall praise Thy works to another: and shall declare Thy mighty acts.

5. I will speak of the glorious honor of Thy majesty: and of Thy wondrous works.

6. And men shall speak of the might of Thy terrible acts: and I will declare Thy greatness.

7. They shall abundantly utter the memory of Thy great goodness: and shall sing of Thy righteousness.

8. *The Lord is gracious and full of compassion: slow to anger and of great mercy.*

9. The Lord is good to all: and His tender mercies are over all His works.

10. *All Thy works shall praise Thee, O Lord: and Thy saints shall bless Thee.*

11. They shall speak of the glory of Thy kingdom: and talk of Thy power,

12. *To make known to the sons of men His mighty acts: and the glorious majesty of His kingdom.*

13. Thy kingdom is an everlasting kingdom: and Thy dominion endureth throughout all generations.

14. *The Lord upholdeth all that fall: and raiseth up all those that be bowed down.*

15. The eyes of all wait upon Thee: and Thou givest them their meat in due season.

16. *Thou openest Thine hand: and satisfiest the desire of every living thing.*

17. The Lord is righteous in all His ways: and holy in all His works.

18. *The Lord is nigh unto all them that call upon Him: to all that call upon Him in truth.*

19. He will fulfill the desire of them that fear Him: He also will hear their cry and will save them.

20. *The Lord preserveth all them that love Him: but all the wicked will He destroy.*

21. My mouth shall speak the praise of the Lord: and let all flesh bless His holy name forever and ever.

Glory be to the Father, etc.

PSALM 150

1. Praise ye the Lord. Praise God in His sanctuary: praise Him in the firmament of His power.

2. *Praise Him for His mighty acts: praise Him according to His excellent greatness.*

47

3. Praise Him with the sound of the trumpet: praise Him with the psaltery and harp.

4. Praise Him with the timbrel and dance: praise Him with stringed instruments and organs.

5. Praise Him upon the loud cymbals: praise Him upon the high-sounding cymbals.

6. Let everything that hath breath praise the Lord: Praise ye the Lord.

Glory be to the Father, etc.

PROVERBS 3:1-6, 9-18

1. My son, forget not My Law: but let thine heart keep My commandments:

2. For length of days, and long life: and peace, shall they add to thee.

3. Let not mercy and truth forsake thee: bind them about thy neck; write them upon the table of thine heart.

4. So shalt thou find favor and good understanding: in the sight of God and man.

5. Trust in the Lord with all thine heart: and lean not unto thine own understanding.

6. In all thy ways acknowledge Him: and He shall direct thy paths.

7. Honor the Lord with thy substance: and with the first fruits of all Thine increase:

8. So shall thy barns be filled with plenty: and thy presses shall burst out with new wine.

9. My son, despise not the chastening of the Lord: neither be weary of His correction;

10. For whom the Lord loveth He correcteth: even as a father the son in whom he delighteth.

11. Happy is the man that findeth wisdom: and the man that getteth understanding.

12. For the merchandise of it is better than the merchandise of silver: and the gain thereof than fine gold.

13. She is more precious than rubies: and all the things thou canst desire are not to be compared unto her.

14. Length of days is in her right hand: and in her left hand riches and honor.

15. Her ways are ways of pleasantness: and all her paths are peace.

16. She is a tree of life to them that lay hold upon her: and happy is everyone that retaineth her.

Glory be to the Father, etc.

ISAIAH 40:1-11

1. Comfort ye, comfort ye My people: saith your God.

2. Speak ye comfortably to Jerusalem, and cry unto her, that her warfare is accomplished, that her iniquity is pardoned: for she hath received of the Lord's hand double for all her sins.

3. The voice of him that crieth in the wilderness: Prepare ye the way of the Lord, make straight in the desert a highway for our God.

4. Every valley shall be exalted, and every mountain and hill shall be made low: and the crooked shall be made straight, and the rough places plain:

5. And the glory of the Lord shall be revealed, and all flesh shall see it together: for the mouth of the Lord hath spoken it.

6. The voice said, Cry, and he said, What shall I cry?: All flesh is grass, and all the goodliness thereof is as the flower of the field.

7. The grass withereth, the flower fadeth: but the Word of our God shall stand forever.

8. O Zion, that bringest good tidings: get thee up into the high mountain: O Jerusalem, that bringest good tidings: lift up thy voice with strength; lift it up, be not afraid: say unto the cities of Judah, Behold your God!

49

9. Behold, the Lord God will come with strong hand: and His arm shall rule for Him.

   10. Behold, His reward is with Him: and His work before Him.

11. He shall feed His flock like a shepherd.

   12. He shall gather the lambs with His arm, and carry them in His bosom: and shall gently lead those that are with young.

Glory be to the Father, etc.

ISAIAH 53:3-6

1. He is despised and rejected of men, a Man of sorrows, and acquainted with grief:

   2. And we hid, as it were, our faces from Him;

3. He was despised,

   4. And we esteemed Him not.

5. Surely He hath borne our griefs and carried our sorrows:

   6. Yet we did esteem Him stricken, smitten of God, and afflicted.

7. But He was wounded for our transgressions, He was bruised for our iniquities:

   8. The chastisement of our peace was upon Him; and with His stripes we are healed.

9. All we like sheep have gone astray; we have turned everyone to his own way;

   10. And the Lord hath laid on Him the iniquity of us all.

Glory be to the Father, etc.

ISAIAH 55:6-11

1. Seek ye the Lord while He may be found, call ye upon Him while He is near.

   2. Let the wicked forsake his way and the unrighteous man his thoughts:

3. And let him return unto the Lord, and He will have mercy upon him;

4. *And to our God, for He will abundantly pardon.*

5. For My thoughts are not your thoughts, neither are your ways My ways, saith the Lord.

6. *For as the heavens are higher than the earth, so are My ways higher than your ways, and My thoughts than your thoughts.*

7. For as the rain cometh down, and the snow, from heaven and returneth not thither;

8. *But watereth the earth and maketh it bring forth and bud, that it may give seed to the sower and bread to the eater:*

9. So shall My Word be that goeth forth out of My mouth. It shall not return unto Me void, but it shall accomplish that which I please,

10. *And it shall prosper in the thing whereto I sent it.*

Glory be to the Father, etc.

MATTHEW 5:3-12

1. Blessed are the poor in spirit: for theirs is the kingdom of heaven.

2. *Blessed are they that mourn: for they shall be comforted.*

3. Blessed are the meek: for they shall inherit the earth.

4. *Blessed are they which do hunger and thirst after righteousness: for they shall be filled.*

5. Blessed are the merciful: for they shall obtain mercy.

6. *Blessed are the pure in heart: for they shall see God.*

7. Blessed are the peacemakers: for they shall be called the children of God.

8. *Blessed are they which are persecuted for righteousness' sake: for theirs is the kingdom of heaven.*

9. Blessed are ye when men shall revile you, and persecute you, and shall say all manner of evil against you falsely, for My sake.

10. Rejoice, and be exceeding glad: for great is your reward in heaven: for so persecuted they the prophets which were before you.

Glory be to the Father, etc.

MATTHEW 6:24-34

1. No man can serve two masters: for either he will hate the one, and love the other; or else he will hold to the one and despise the other: Ye cannot serve God and mammon.

2. Therefore I say unto you, Take no thought for your life, what ye shall eat or what ye shall drink; nor yet for your body, what ye shall put on. Is not the life more than meat and the body than raiment?

3. Behold the fowls of the air: for they sow not, neither do they reap, nor gather into barns;

4. Yet your heavenly Father feedeth them. Are ye not much better than they?

5. Which of you by taking thought can add one cubit unto his stature?

6. And why take ye thought for raiment? Consider the lilies of the field, how they grow; they toil not, neither do they spin:

7. And yet I say unto you that even Solomon in all his glory was not arrayed like one of these.

8. Wherefore, if God so clothe the grass of the field, which today is, and tomorrow is cast into the oven, shall He not much more clothe you, O ye of little faith?

52

9. Therefore take no thought, saying: What shall we eat? or, What shall we drink? or, Wherewithal shall we be clothed?

10. For after all these things do the Gentiles seek: for your heavenly Father knoweth that ye have need of all these things.

11. But seek ye first the kingdom of God, and His righteousness; and all these things shall be added unto you.

12. Take therefore no thought for the morrow: for the morrow shall take thought for the things of itself. Sufficient unto the day is the evil thereof.

Glory be to the Father, etc.

MATTHEW 10:28-33, 37-40, 42

1. Fear not them which kill the body, but are not able to kill the soul.

2. But rather fear Him which is able to destroy both soul and body in hell.

3. Are not two sparrows sold for a farthing? And one of them shall not fall on the ground without your Father.

4. But the very hairs of your head are all numbered.

5. Fear ye not, therefore; ye are of more value than many sparrows.

6. Whosoever therefore shall confess Me before men, him will I confess also before My Father which is in heaven.

7. But whosoever shall deny Me before men, him will I also deny before My Father which is in heaven.

8. He that loveth father or mother more than Me is not worthy of Me:

9. And he that loveth son or daughter more than Me is not worthy of Me.

10. And he that taketh not his cross, and followeth after Me, is not worthy of Me.

11. He that findeth his life shall lose it:

12. And he that loseth his life for My sake shall find it.

13. He that receiveth you receiveth Me, and he that receiveth Me receiveth Him that sent Me.

14. And whosoever shall give to drink unto one of these little ones a cup of cold water only in the name of a disciple, verily I say unto you he shall in no wise lose his reward.

Glory be to the Father, etc.

JOHN 14:1-6

1. Let not your heart be troubled: ye believe in God, believe also in Me.

2. In My Father's house are many mansions; if it were not so, I would have told you.

3. I go to prepare a place for you.

4. And if I go and prepare a place for you, I will come again and receive you unto Myself; that where I am, there ye may be also.

5. And whither I go ye know, and the way ye know.

6. Thomas saith unto Him, Lord, we know not whither Thou goest; and how can we know the way?

7. Jesus saith unto him: I am the Way, the Truth, and the Life;

8. No man cometh unto the Father but by Me.

Glory be to the Father, etc.

JOHN 15:1-8

1. I am the true Vine, and My Father is the Husbandman.

2. Every branch in Me that beareth not fruit He taketh away; and every branch that beareth fruit, He purgeth it, that it may bring forth more fruit.

3. Now ye are clean through the Word, which I have spoken unto you.

4. Abide in Me, and I in you. As the branch cannot bear fruit of itself, except it abide in the vine; no more can ye except ye abide in Me.

5. I am the Vine, ye are the branches. He that abideth in Me, and I in him, the same bringeth forth much fruit; for without Me ye can do nothing.

6. *If a man abide not in Me, he is cast forth as a branch and is withered; and men gather them and cast them into the fire, and they are burned.*

7. If ye abide in Me, and My words abide in you, ye shall ask what ye will, and it shall be done unto you.

8. *Herein is My Father glorified, that ye bear much fruit; so shall ye be My disciples.*

Glory be to the Father, etc.

PHILIPPIANS 2:5-11

1. Let this mind be in you, which was also in Christ Jesus:

2. *Who, being in the form of God, thought it not robbery to be equal with God;*

3. But made Himself of no reputation, and took upon Him the form of a servant,

4. *And was made in the likeness of men.*

5. And being found in fashion as a man, He humbled Himself and became obedient unto death, even the death of the cross.

6. *Wherefore God also hath highly exalted Him and given Him a name which is above every name,*

7. That at the name of Jesus every knee should bow, of things in heaven, and things in earth, and things under the earth,

8. *And that every tongue should confess that Jesus Christ is Lord, to the glory of God the Father.*

Glory be to the Father, etc.

1 JOHN 1:5-10

1. This, then, is the message which we have heard of Him and declare unto you, that God is Light and in Him is no darkness at all.

2. If we say that we have fellowship with Him and walk in darkness, we lie, and do not the truth.

3. But if we walk in the light, as He is in the light, we have fellowship one with another;

4. And the blood of Jesus Christ, His Son, cleanseth us from all sin.

5. If we say that we have no sin, we deceive ourselves, and the truth is not in us.

6. If we confess our sins, He is faithful and just to forgive us our sins and to cleanse us from all unrighteousness.

7. If we say that we have not sinned, we make Him a liar;
8. And His Word is not in us.

Glory be to the Father, etc.

1 JOHN 4:7-16

1. Beloved, let us love one another; for love is of God, and everyone that loveth is born of God and knoweth God.

2. He that loveth not knoweth not God; for God is Love.

3. In this was manifested the love of God toward us, because that God sent His only-begotten Son into the world that we might live through Him.

4. Herein is love, not that we loved God, but that He loved us, and sent His Son to be the Propitiation for our sins.

5. Beloved, if God so loved us, we ought also to love one another.

6. No man hath seen God at any time. If we love one another, God dwelleth in us, and His love is perfected in us.

7. Hereby know we that we dwell in Him and He in us, because He has given us of His Spirit.

8. And we have seen and do testify that the Father sent the Son to be the Savior of the world.

9. Whosoever shall confess that Jesus is the Son of God, God dwelleth in him and he in God.

10. *And we have known and believed the love that God hath to us. God is Love; and he that dwelleth in love dwelleth in God, and God in him.*

Glory be to the Father, etc.

REVELATION 7:9-17

1. After this I beheld, and, lo, a great multitude, which no man could number, of all nations, and kindreds, and people, and tongues, stood before the throne, and before the Lamb, clothed with white robes and palms in their hands;

2. *And cried with a loud voice, saying: Salvation to our God, which sitteth upon the throne, and unto the Lamb.*

3. And all the angels stood round about the throne, and about the elders and the four beasts, and fell before the throne on their faces, and worshiped God,

4. *Saying: Amen, blessing, and glory, and wisdom, and thanksgiving, and honor, and power, and might, be unto our God forever and ever. Amen.*

5. And one of the elders answered, saying unto me, What are these which are arrayed in white robes? And whence came they?

6. *And I said unto him, Sir, thou knowest.*

7. And he said to me: These are they which came out of great tribulation and have washed their robes and made them white in the blood of the Lamb.

8. *Therefore are they before the throne of God and serve Him day and night in His temple; and He that sitteth on the throne shall dwell among them.*

9. They shall hunger no more, neither thirst any more; neither shall the sun light on them nor any heat.

10. *For the Lamb which is in the midst of the throne shall feed them and shall lead them unto living fountains of waters; and God shall wipe away all tears from their eyes.*

Glory be to the Father, etc.

57

Luther's SMALL CATECHISM

I. The Ten Commandments

THE FIRST COMMANDMENT

Thou shalt have no other gods before Me.

What does this mean?

We should fear, love, and trust in God above all things.

THE SECOND COMMANDMENT

Thou shalt not take the name of the LORD, thy God, in vain.

What does this mean?

We should fear and love God that we may not curse, swear, use witchcraft, lie or deceive by His name, but call upon it in every trouble, pray, praise, and give thanks.

THE THIRD COMMANDMENT

Remember the Sabbath day, to keep it holy.

What does this mean?

We should fear and love God that we may not despise preaching and His Word, but hold it sacred and gladly hear and learn it.

THE FOURTH COMMANDMENT

Thou shalt honor thy father and thy mother, that it may be well with thee, and thou mayest live long on the earth.

What does this mean?

We should fear and love God that we may not despise our parents and masters nor provoke them to anger, but give them honor, serve and obey them, and hold them in love and esteem.

THE FIFTH COMMANDMENT

Thou shalt not kill.

What does this mean?

We should fear and love God that we may not hurt nor harm our neighbor in his body, but help and befriend him in every bodily need.

THE SIXTH COMMANDMENT

Thou shalt not commit adultery.

What does this mean?

We should fear and love God that we may lead a chaste and decent life in word and deed and each love and honor his spouse.

THE SEVENTH COMMANDMENT

Thou shalt not steal.

What does this mean?

We should fear and love God that we may not take our neighbor's money or goods, nor get them by false ware or dealing, but help him to improve and protect his property and business.

THE EIGHTH COMMANDMENT

Thou shalt not bear false witness against thy neighbor.

What does this mean?

We should fear and love God that we may not deceitfully belie, betray, slander, nor defame our neighbor, but defend him, speak well of him, and put the best construction on everything.

THE NINTH COMMANDMENT

Thou shalt not covet thy neighbor's house.

What does this mean?

We should fear and love God that we may not craftily seek to get our neighbor's inheritance or house, nor obtain it by a show of right, but help and be of service to him in keeping it.

THE TENTH COMMANDMENT

Thou shalt not covet thy neighbor's wife, nor his manservant, nor his maidservant, nor his cattle, nor anything that is thy neighbor's.

What does this mean?

We should fear and love God that we may not estrange, force, or entice away from our neighbor his wife, servants, or cattle, but urge them to stay and do their duty.

What does God say of all these Commandments?

He says thus: I the Lord, thy God, am a jealous God, visiting the iniquity of the fathers upon the children unto the third and fourth generation of them that hate Me, and showing mercy unto thousands of them that love Me and keep My Commandments.

What does this mean?

God threatens to punish all that transgress these Commandments. Therefore we should fear His wrath and not act contrary to them. But He promises grace and every blessing to all that keep these Commandments. Therefore we should also love and trust in Him and willingly do according to His Commandments.

II. The Creed

I believe in God the Father Almighty, Maker of heaven and earth.

What does this mean?

I believe that God has made me and all creatures; that He has given me my body and soul, eyes, ears, and all my members, my reason and all my senses, and still preserves them; also clothing and shoes, meat and drink, house and home, wife and children, fields, cattle, and all my goods; that He richly and daily provides me with all that I need to support this body and life; that He defends me against all danger and guards and protects me from all evil; and all this purely out of fatherly, divine goodness and mercy, without any merit or worthiness in me; for all which it is my duty to thank and praise, to serve and obey Him. This is most certainly true.

THE SECOND ARTICLE

And in Jesus Christ, His only Son, our Lord, who was conceived by the Holy Ghost, born of the Virgin Mary, suffered under Pontius Pilate, was crucified, dead, and buried; He descended into hell; the third day He rose again from the dead; He ascended into heaven and sitteth on the right hand of God the Father Almighty, from thence He shall come to judge the quick and the dead.

What does this mean?

I believe that Jesus Christ, true God, begotten of the Father from eternity, and also true man, born of the Virgin Mary, is my Lord, who has redeemed me, a lost and condemned creature, purchased and won me from all sins, from death, and from the power of the devil; not with gold or silver, but with His holy, precious blood and with His innocent suffering and death, that I may be

His own and live under Him in His kingdom, and serve Him in everlasting righteousness, innocence, and blessedness, even as He is risen from the dead, lives and reigns to all eternity. This is most certainly true.

THE THIRD ARTICLE

I believe in the Holy Ghost; the holy Christian Church, the communion of saints; the forgiveness of sins; the resurrection of the body; and the life everlasting. Amen.

What does this mean?

I believe that I cannot by my own reason or strength believe in Jesus Christ, my Lord, or come to Him; but the Holy Ghost has called me by the Gospel, enlightened me with His gifts, sanctified and kept me in the true faith; even as He calls, gathers, enlightens, and sanctifies the whole Christian Church on earth and keeps it with Jesus Christ in the one true faith; in which Christian Church He daily and richly forgives all sins to me and all believers, and will at the Last Day raise up me and all the dead, and give unto me and all believers in Christ eternal life. This is most certainly true.

III. The Lord's Prayer

THE INTRODUCTION

Our Father who art in heaven.

What does this mean?

God would by these words tenderly invite us to believe that He is our true Father, and that we are His true children, so that we may with all boldness and confidence ask Him as dear children ask their dear father.

THE FIRST PETITION

Hallowed be Thy name.

What does this mean?

God's name is indeed holy in itself; but we pray in this petition that it may be holy among us also.

How is this done?

When the Word of God is taught in its truth and purity, and we, as the children of God, also lead a holy life according to it. This grant us, dear Father in heaven. But he that teaches and lives otherwise than God's Word teaches, profanes the name of God among us. From this preserve us, heavenly Father.

THE SECOND PETITION

Thy kingdom come.

What does this mean?

The kingdom of God comes indeed without our prayer, of itself; but we pray in this petition that it may come unto us also.

How is this done?

When our heavenly Father gives us His Holy Spirit, so that by His grace we believe His holy Word and lead a godly life, here in time and hereafter in eternity.

THE THIRD PETITION

Thy will be done on earth as it is in heaven.

What does this mean?

The good and gracious will of God is done indeed without our prayer; but we pray in this petition that it may be done among us also.

How is this done?

When God breaks and hinders every evil counsel and will which would not let us hallow God's name nor let His kingdom come, such as the will of the devil, the world, and our flesh; but strengthens and preserves us steadfast in His Word and faith unto our end. This is His gracious and good will.

Give us this day our daily bread.

What does this mean?

God gives daily bread indeed without our prayer, also to all the wicked; but we pray in this petition that He would lead us to know it and to receive our daily bread with thanksgiving.

What is meant by daily bread?

Everything that belongs to the support and wants of the body, such as food, drink, clothing, shoes, house, home, field, cattle, money, goods, a pious spouse, pious children, pious servants, pious and faithful rulers, good government, good weather, peace, health, discipline, honor, good friends, faithful neighbors, and the like.

THE FIFTH PETITION

And forgive us our trespasses, as we forgive those who trespass against us.

What does this mean?

We pray in this petition that our Father in heaven would not look upon our sins, nor on their account deny our prayer; for we are worthy of none of the things for which we pray, neither have we deserved them; but that He would grant them all to us by grace; for we daily sin much and indeed deserve nothing but punishment. So will we also heartily forgive, and readily do good to those who sin against us.

THE SIXTH PETITION

And lead us not into temptation.

What does this mean?

God indeed tempts no one; but we pray in this petition that God would guard and keep us, so that the devil, the world, and our flesh may not deceive us nor seduce us into misbelief, despair, and other great shame and vice; and though we be assailed by them, that still we may finally overcome and obtain the victory.

But deliver us from evil.

What does this mean?

We pray in this petition, as the sum of all, that our Father in heaven would deliver us from every evil of body and soul, property and honor, and finally, when our last hour has come, grant us a blessed end, and graciously take us from this vale of tears to Himself in heaven.

THE CONCLUSION

For Thine is the kingdom and the power and the glory forever and ever. Amen.

What is meant by the word "Amen"?

That I should be certain that these petitions are acceptable to our Father in heaven and heard by Him; for He Himself has commanded us so to pray, and has promised to hear us. Amen, Amen, that is Yea, yea, it shall be so.

IV. The Sacrament of Holy Baptism

I THE NATURE OF BAPTISM

What is Baptism?

Baptism is not simple water only, but it is the water comprehended in God's command and connected with God's word.

Which is that word of God?

Christ, our Lord, says in the last chapter of Matthew: *Go ye and teach all nations, baptizing them in the name of the Father and of the Son and of the Holy Ghost.*

What does Baptism give or profit?

It works forgiveness of sins, delivers from death and the devil, and gives eternal salvation to all who believe this, as the words and promises of God declare.

Which are such words and promises of God?

Christ, our Lord, says in the last chapter of Mark: *He that believeth and is baptized, shall be saved; but he that believeth not, shall be damned.*

III THE POWER OF BAPTISM

How can water do such great things?

It is not the water indeed that does them, but the word of God which is in and with the water, and faith, which trusts such word of God in the water. For without the word of God the water is simple water and no Baptism. But with the word of God it is a Baptism, that is, a gracious water of life and a washing of regeneration in the Holy Ghost, as St. Paul says, Titus, chapter third: [According to His mercy He saved us] *By the washing of regeneration and renewing of the Holy Ghost, which He shed on us abundantly through Jesus Christ, our Savior, that, being justified by His grace, we should be made heirs according to the hope of eternal life. This is a faithful saying.*

IV THE SIGNIFICANCE OF BAPTIZING WITH WATER

What does such baptizing with water signify?

It signifies that the Old Adam in us should, by daily contrition and repentance, be drowned and die with all sins and evil lusts and, again, a new man daily come forth and arise, who shall live before God in righteousness and purity forever.

Where is this written?

St. Paul says, Romans, chapter sixth: *We are buried with Christ by Baptism into death, that, like as He was raised up from the dead by the glory of the Father, even so we also should walk in newness of life.*

V. The Office of the Keys and Confession

What is the Office of the Keys?

It is the peculiar church power which Christ has given to His Church on earth to forgive the sins of penitent sinners unto them, but to retain the sins of the impenitent as long as they do not repent.

Where is this written?

Thus writes the holy Evangelist John, chapter twentieth: *The Lord Jesus breathed on His disciples and saith unto them, Receive ye the Holy Ghost. Whosesoever sins ye remit, they are remitted unto them; and whosesoever sins ye retain, they are retained.*

What do you believe according to these words?

I believe that, when the called ministers of Christ deal with us by His divine command, especially when they exclude manifest and impenitent sinners from the Christian congregation, and, again, when they absolve those who repent of their sins and are willing to amend, this is as valid and certain, in heaven also, as if Christ, our dear Lord, dealt with us Himself.

What is Confession?

Confession embraces two parts: One is that we confess our sins; the other, that we receive absolution, or forgiveness, from the pastor as from God Himself, and in no wise doubt, but firmly believe, that by it our sins are forgiven before God in heaven.

What sins should we confess?

Before God we should plead guilty of all sins, even of those which we do not know, as we do in the Lord's Prayer; but before the pastor we should confess those sins only which we know and feel in our hearts.

Which are these?

Here consider your station according to the Ten Commandments, whether you are a father, mother, son, daughter, master, mistress, servant; whether you have been disobedient, unfaithful, slothful; whether you have grieved any person by word or deed; whether you have stolen, neglected, or wasted aught, or done other injury.

VI. The Sacrament of the Altar

What is the Sacrament of the Altar?

It is the true body and blood of our Lord Jesus Christ under the bread and wine, for us Christians to eat and to drink, instituted by Christ Himself.

Where is this written?

The holy Evangelists Matthew, Mark, Luke, and St. Paul [the Apostle] write thus:

Our Lord Jesus Christ, the same night in which He was betrayed, took bread; and when He had given thanks, He brake it and gave it to His disciples, saying, Take eat; this is My body, which is given for you. This do in remembrance of Me.

After the same manner also He took the cup when He had supped, and when He had given thanks, He gave it to them, saying, Drink ye all of it; this cup is the new testament in My blood, which is shed for you for the remission of sins. This do, as oft as ye drink it, in remembrance of Me.

What is the benefit of such eating and drinking?

That is shown us by these words, "Given and shed for you for the remission of sins"; namely, that in the Sacrament forgiveness of sins, life, and salvation are given us through these words. For where there is forgiveness of sins, there is also life and salvation.

How can bodily eating and drinking do such great things?

It is not the eating and drinking indeed that does them, but the words here written, *Given and shed for you for the remission of sins;* which words, besides the bodily eating and drinking, are the chief thing in the Sacrament; and he that believes these words has what they say and express, namely, the forgiveness of sins.

Who, then, receives such Sacrament worthily?

Fasting and bodily preparation are indeed a fine outward training; but he is truly worthy and well prepared who has faith in these words, *Given and shed for you for the remission of sins.* But he that does not believe these words, or doubts, is unworthy and unprepared; for the words "for you" require all hearts to believe.

The PRAYERS

I. General Prayers

1

Dear heavenly Father, we thank Thee for the opportunity to meet again in Thy house in order to study Thy Word, to tell Thee our needs, and to receive instruction for our Christian life. May we all realize that we are in Thy presence and honor Thee by being quiet and respectful. Help us to understand Thy Word and grant us grace to keep it in our hearts and to be guided by it in all that we say or do. Hear us for the sake of our Savior Jesus. Amen.

2

Dear heavenly Father, as we come into Thy presence this morning, we thank Thee for giving us parents who care for us, and also clothing, food, and shelter. We thank Thee for the Scriptures, which are able to make us wise unto salvation through faith which is in Christ Jesus. May the Bible, Thy holy Word, be more precious to us than all riches, and grant us Thy Holy Spirit that we may believe in Jesus and follow His example in our daily life. Hear us for Jesus' sake. Amen.

3

We thank Thee, our God and Father, for permitting us to gather once more in this sacred place to sing and pray together, and to receive instruction in the truths of the Bible. Help us to put away all worldly thoughts and needless worries and to give our attention to the things which Thou wouldst have us learn. Bless us as we listen to our teachers. Through the week may we always do Thy will. Hear us for Jesus' sake. Amen.

4

Lord Jesus, Thou art the great Prophet and Teacher foretold by Moses. Thou didst come from above to make known to us the saving truths of the Gospel and to lead us on the way to heaven. Help us to attend to the one thing needful, to follow Mary's example, and to listen with quiet attention when Thy Word is being taught. May we then also follow Martha's example and go forth to another week of serving Thee in all that we do. Thou who hast died to save us, hear us. Amen.

5

O Thou righteous God, we come before Thee as guilty sinners who have disobeyed Thy Commandments and deserve to be punished. But we come as Thy dear children, trusting in Jesus, who died to save us. Open our hearts today to receive and understand and keep Thy Word. Enable us also in our daily behavior to set a good example and to show that we are Thy trusting children; in Jesus' name. Amen.

6

Dear heavenly Father, be with us today as we sing the praises of Him who died for us, as we pray and give thanks, and receive instruction from Thy Word. Grant that we all may be thoughtful and reverent in Thy house. May Thy Holy Spirit dwell in our hearts and enable us to grasp the lesson which is taught us and to obey it during the week. We ask this for Jesus' sake. Amen.

7

We thank Thee, Lord, for the blessings Thou hast given us through the Church. We praise Thee especially for the Bible, which tells us of the Savior who died for sinners and teaches us to live as Thy children. Bless our parents and teachers who explain Thy Word to us, and lead us in the delightful road of obedience. Help us every day by such obedience to set a good example for others. In Jesus' name, we pray. Amen.

8

Lord Jesus, Thou art the Good Shepherd and hast laid down Thy life to save us from our sins. For Thy great love we thank Thee, dear Savior. Feed our souls in the green pastures of Thy Word and help us to grow in knowledge, holiness, and all that is pleasing to Thee. Keep us from straying into sinful ways, and mercifully bring us back to the fold when we stray. Keep us faithful in trials and temptations and take us at last to Thee in heaven. Amen.

9

Dear Lord, we praise Thee for the many undeserved blessings Thou hast given us to enjoy. Above all, we thank Thee for the Bible which shows us our sinfulness, leads us to saving faith in Jesus, and prompts us to follow His holy example. Grant us grace to listen with respect and close attention to our teachers, so that Thy Word may keep us aware of our sinfulness and of our only Savior Jesus. Strengthen our faith, and enable us to grow more holy and righteous. We ask it in the name of Him who died for us. Amen.

10

Precious Jesus, who hast said, "Let the little children come unto Me and forbid them not," we are happy in knowing Thy great love for us. We thank Thee for parents and others who teach us the Bible and have led us into Thy waiting arms. Keep us from harm and danger. When we are tempted, make us strong to resist. Help us to understand and remember Thy Word and always to do what it tells us. Have mercy on the children who do not know Thee and help us to bring them to Thee. Graciously hear us. Amen.

11

We thank Thee, dear heavenly Father, for the Bible which tells us of Thy love in sending Thy Son Jesus to be the Savior of all people. Lead us all to feel our sinfulness and our need of a Savior and to go to Him for forgiveness and strength. We thank Thee also for Thy Commandments which show us how Christians are to live in order to please Thee. Help us to remember these Commandments and to make them our rule for daily living. Hear us for Jesus' sake. Amen.

12

O God, how great is Thy goodness for giving us every week a day on which to rest and prepare for another week. Help us to appreciate Sunday chiefly because it gives us an opportunity to hear the Gospel of our Savior, Jesus Christ, and to receive guidance for our daily living. Grant that each one present may be reverent and attentive in behavior during worship and the study of Thy Word. May we all leave Thy house joyful and strengthened in our desire to do Thy will. Hear us for Jesus' sake. Amen.

II. Seasonal Prayers

ADVENT

Dear heavenly Father, in this blessed Advent season, we remember Thy gracious promises of old that a Savior would come. We thank Thee for fulfilling these promises by sending Thy dearly beloved Son, Jesus Christ, to become a human being for our sakes, and to redeem us from sin, death, and eternal misery. Help us during this Advent season to repent of our sins, to cling with firm faith to Jesus our Savior, to follow His holy example, and thus to prepare for Christmas. Grant us grace so to live that we may always be prepared for that great day when heaven and earth will pass away. When the Lord Jesus will come again to judge the living and the dead, may He take us with all His loved ones to Himself in heaven. Hear us, for Jesus' sake. Amen.

Blessed Christ Child, we kneel reverently at Thy manger bed on this day of Thy birth, for we know that Thou, though a weak and helpless Babe, art the almighty Son of God by whom the world was made. How great is Thy love for us in becoming a Child in order to redeem us from sin and eternal death! For Thy grace and mercy we thank Thee, dear Lord. We pray Thee, live in our hearts. Cleanse us from sin, and help us to serve Thee in holiness and righteousness all the days of our life. Fill us with love toward others, and make us willing to share both the treasure of the Gospel and our earthly blessings with those who are poor and sick in body and soul. For Thy name's sake, we ask it. Amen.

ON ENTERING THE NEW YEAR

Dear heavenly Father, how great is Thy love and compassion for us poor sinners! Although we have often been unfaithful to Thee during the past year, Thou hast not forsaken us. In spite of our sins, Thou hast given us many good things to enjoy and hast spared us much suffering and misfortune. For all the blessings of Thy goodness, we thank Thee, dear Lord. And as we enter the new year, we look to Thee for strength and guidance. Forgive our sins for Jesus' sake. Help us to win the victory over temptation and to serve Thee faithfully in the new year. Be Thou our Refuge and Helper all the days of our life. We ask it in Jesus' name. Amen.

Dear Savior, as we enter the new year, we think of that day when, as a little child, Thou didst receive the name Jesus. We are thankful for this name, which tells us that Thou art our Savior from sin and our Helper in every trouble. May the name Jesus always be dear to us, and may we through faith in Thee be happy from day to day, knowing that our sins are forgiven. Grant us courage to bear whatever sorrows may come upon us in the new year, and enable us to walk with Thee in the path that leads to everlasting life. Amen.

EPIPHANY

We thank Thee, dear heavenly Father, for guiding the Wise Men by a wonderful star to the birthplace of our Savior-King. Because of Thy mercy to these Gentiles, we know that Jesus came to save both the Jews and the Gentiles. We confess Thee as our Savior and we worship Thee as our God and our King. We pray also that the good news of forgiveness and salvation may be spread in all the world and that the Gentiles everywhere may be brought to faith in Thee. Amen.

LENT

Lord Jesus Christ, we thank Thee for Thy great love which moved Thee to suffer under Pontius Pilate and to die on the cross in order to save us and all people from the curse and punishment of sin. Grant that this sacred season of Lent may be a blessing to every one. By means of Thy Word lead us to a deeper knowledge of our sinful hearts and fill us with true sorrow over the transgressions which caused Thy great pain and Thy death. Strengthen our faith as we again see Thee beaten and crowned with thorns and crucified. Help us to show our love and gratitude to Thee by shunning sin and by doing only those things which are well pleasing to Thee. Lord Jesus, we give ourselves to Thee. Help us to live to Thy glory. Amen.

PALM SUNDAY

Dear Savior, on that first Palm Sunday Thou didst ride into Jerusalem as King amid the glad hosannas of the people. Today we again welcome Thee with songs of praise as Thou comest to bless us. Grant that we may be truly sorry for our sins and may trust in Thee for forgiveness and for strength. Dear Lord, we would serve Thee with our hearts and voices, with our hands and feet, with all our powers. Grant also that they who kneel at Thy altar today confessing their faith in Thee may remain faithful even unto death, and receive a crown of life. In mercy, hear us. Amen.

Lord Jesus Christ, our risen Savior, our hearts overflow with joy on this glorious Easter Day, because the heavenly Father raised Thee from the dead. We bless Thee for the assurance that our sins are forgiven and that we have everlasting life in Thee. We thank and praise Thee, blessed Savior, for the forgiveness and salvation Thou hast purchased for us by Thy suffering and death on the cross. And as Thou didst rise from the grave with a glorified body, grant that we, Thy children, may forsake sin and live a beautiful Christian life. Help us to remember that Thou art the ever-living Savior to whom we may go in every trouble and temptation. Keep us in Thy love, and, through a blessed death, take us to Thyself in heaven, where we shall live with Thee forever in perfect joy. Amen.

ASCENSION

Lord Jesus Christ, we rejoice today because Thou didst ascend into heaven a victor over sin, death, and the devil. We know that Thou art seated at the right hand of God and rulest over all things. Though we see Thee no longer, help us to remember that Thou art invisibly present with us always, to guide and protect us, and to enable us to love and serve Thee. May we daily obtain strength from Thee to do the will of our heavenly Father. Do Thou also bless the missionaries who are telling sinners of Thy love, and cause many of the lost to put their trust in Thee. Amen.

PENTECOST

Dear Holy Spirit, on this day of Pentecost we confess that we cannot by our own reason or strength repent and believe in Jesus, our Savior. But we know that Thou hast called us by the Gospel and given us saving faith. Alas! We are still weak and ignorant and often do wrong because of our sinful hearts. Therefore we pray Thee, dwell in our hearts and grant us true love of the Savior, so that we may shun everything wicked and grow in godliness and good works. Help us to serve Thee with all our powers. For Jesus' sake. Amen.

TRINITY

O Thou eternal God, Father, Son, and Holy Spirit, on this blessed Trinity Sunday we confess our faith in Thee and worship Thee, the only true God. We thank Thee, God the Father, for all the good things Thou hast given us to enjoy in this world. We thank Thee, God the Son, for Thy great love in coming to redeem us by Thy holy life and Thy innocent suffering and death. We thank Thee, God the Holy Spirit, for leading us to a knowledge of our sins and to faith in Jesus, our Savior. Keep us in true faith and enable us to serve Thee in holiness now and forever. Amen.

REFORMATION DAY

Dear heavenly Father, we thank Thee that Thou didst prepare Martin Luther to deliver the Church from ignorance and superstition and to give us the Bible and the saving truths of Thy holy Word. Because we have Thy Word, we know that we cannot be saved by our good works. We know, too, that through faith in Jesus, our only Savior, we have forgiveness of all sins and eternal salvation. Preserve us from false teachers who would destroy our souls. Cause Thy Gospel to be preached everywhere and to bring forgiveness and peace to those who are still in darkness. Grant that we may be diligent students of Thy Word and help us to live holy lives. Thus may we show our thankfulness to Thee for the blessings Thou hast given us through the Reformation. We ask it in the name of Jesus, who died to save us. Amen.

THANKSGIVING DAY

Merciful Father, in this season of thanksgiving we acknowledge that all the products of field, orchard, garden, mill and factory are the gift of Thy goodness. We are not worthy of the least of Thy blessings, for we are sinful by nature. But Thou hast made us Thy children through faith in Jesus Christ and dost deal mercifully with us for His sake. Help us to be thankful for the Bible, the Church, and other blessings; and for all Thy earthly gifts. Give us contented hearts, and willingness also to share what we have with the poor. May we not only praise Thee with our lips, but may we also show by our behavior that we love Thee and appreciate Thy goodness. In Jesus' name, we ask it. Amen.

III. Special Prayers

AT THE BEGINNING OF ANOTHER SCHOOL YEAR

Dear heavenly Father, who hast permitted us to begin another year of worship and study, we thank Thee for the blessings which have come to us in the past. Continue to bless us as we study Thy Word. Give to the teachers the wisdom and ability they need to teach and apply Thy Word well. Grant that the children may be prompt and regular in their attendance, study their lessons diligently, and in their everyday lives practice what they learn. Help all of us to be respectful, friendly, and obedient, knowing that Thou art present among us and ready to bless those who open their hearts to Thy Word. Fill us with love toward those still lost in sin because no one has ever told them of Jesus, their Savior. Help all of us, teachers and pupils, to win many souls for Jesus, who died on the cross for the sins of the whole world. In His name, we ask it. Amen.

FOR ALL CHILDREN

Dear Lord, we pray for all children. All have been redeemed by the blood of Jesus, and are therefore precious in Thy sight. Bring them to the knowledge of the Truth, that they may know their Savior and trust in Him. Give them faithful teachers who will instruct them further in the saving truths of the Bible. Warn them against wrongdoing, and teach them by word and example to live as Christians in this wicked world. Fill their hearts with true love of Thy Word and prompt them to study it thoughtfully. Enable them to honor and obey their parents, teachers, and government, to work and study well, and to develop and use their talents for Thee. Dear Savior, keep the children close to Thee, and let none of them perish, but bring them to their eternal home in heaven, for Jesus' sake. Amen.

FOR THE PASTORS AND TEACHERS OF THE CHURCH

Dear heavenly Father, we pray for the men and women who have been called to teach Thy holy Word and to lead others in the way of faith and love. Do Thou by Thy Holy Spirit enable them to understand the teachings of the Bible and to express them in simple language that others can grasp. Give them wisdom to present Jesus as the only Savior of sinners and to teach the commandments according to which we are to live as Thy dear children. Grant that we may be respectful and profitable hearers and that we may remember and do what the Bible teaches. Hear us for Jesus' sake. Amen.

FOR THE CHURCH AND ITS PASTORS AND TEACHERS

O Thou eternal God, we thank Thee for the blessings Thou hast given us through the Church and through the pastors and teachers who make known to us the great truths of the Bible. Protect the Church from the cruel enemies who wish to destroy it. Cause the Church to spread until millions more will believe in the Savior who died on the Cross for all. Bless all faithful pastors and teachers. Grant them wisdom to teach Thy Word well and in truth and purity. Give them patience to guide the weak, and courage to endure whatever hardships Thou wilt be pleased to send them. Hear us for Jesus' sake. Amen.

FOR THE CATECHUMENS

Blessed Savior, we pray for all who are being instructed by pastors and teachers and are being prepared for active membership in the congregation through the study of Thy Word. Give to all catechumens willing hearts and eager minds to learn the truths of the Bible and to live according to these truths. Dear Savior, preserve them from all forms of dishonesty and hypocrisy and keep them sincere in their faith. Fill them with love toward Thee and grant that they may become more and more like Thee in purity and in all that is good. May they serve Thee and be with Thee forever in glory. Amen.

FOR THOSE WHO DO NOT KNOW JESUS

Lord Jesus Christ, how blessed are we who have learned of Thy great love and now love Thee in return as our best Friend and only Savior! Alas, there are millions of children who have never learned of Thy love because no one has invited them to hear Thy Word. Dear Savior, have mercy on these children, many of whom are living in sin and shame and are being misled into crime. Forgive us our failure to be workers for Thee, and grant that at least a few children may be won through our efforts. Help each one of us to be a soulwinner. Give us courage to tell others of Thy love, and to bring them to hear and learn Thy Word. Grant us grace so to live that others may see our good example and may be led to faith in Thee. For Thy name's sake, hear us. Amen.

FOR THE SICK

Lord Jesus Christ, who during Thy earthly life didst mercifully heal the sick and comfort the sorrowing, Thou art to this day a very present Help in trouble. Thou dost pity the sick and afflicted and hast promised to hear our prayer for them. Dear Savior, we pray for _____ who is sick and in need of Thy divine help. Be present with _____ in his (her) illness, and if it be Thy will graciously restore him (her) soon to health again. Bless all who are sick and afflicted. Give them patient and cheerful hearts. Grant that they may be drawn closer to Thee through their sickness, and may they serve Thee the more faithfully when they are well again. Be pleased to hear our prayer. Amen.

Lord Jesus Christ, our Friend and Savior, we ask Thee to look with favor upon our homes and to bless parents and children, and all who dwell in the home. Cause Thy Word, the holy Bible, to be read diligently by young and old, and may this be the means of keeping our homes pure and pleasant and peaceful. Cause parents to bring up their children in the fear of the Lord. Help us to be respectful and obedient, kind and thoughtful, meek and forgiving, always seeking to please Thee and trying to make our parents and others happy. Lord Jesus, we invite Thee to be the ever present Guest in our homes, and help us, we pray Thee, always to remember that Thou art present and ready to bless all who love Thee and do Thy will. Hear our prayer, gracious Savior. Amen.

ON A BIRTHDAY

Dear heavenly Father, we thank Thee that Thou hast graciously permitted ＿＿＿＿＿ to come to the end of another year in *his (her, their) earthly life (lives)* and to celebrate *his (her, their) birthday (birthdays)* today. We are grateful to Thee for the many blessings showered upon *him (her, them)*. We thank Thee, in particular, for permitting *him (her, them)* to know Jesus as the heavenly Friend and Savior, and for leading *him (her, them)* to believe in Him and to love and serve Him. Continue to give *him (her, them)* good things to enjoy. But above all else, keep *him (her, them)* from wrongdoing and enable *him (her, them)* to be faithful in hearing and learning Thy Word and in doing Thy will. We ask this in Jesus' name. Amen.

ON WASHINGTON'S BIRTHDAY

Eternal God, Lord of the nations, we praise and thank Thee for raising up wise and noble leaders like George Washington who defend our country and give us the protection of good government. We confess that we are unworthy of the precious freedom and of the many other blessings we enjoy under the flag of our country. We pray Thee, mercifully forgive our sins, help us to serve Thee faithfully, and let Thy favor rest upon us continually. Bring to repentance and faith all who are still living in sin and wickedness. Bless our country with wise and able rulers. Preserve for us freedom of religion and freedom of worship. Cause Thy Church to prosper and grow and to gather in a rich harvest of souls for heaven. We ask it in the name of the Savior, who died for all. Amen.

ON LINCOLN'S BIRTHDAY

O God, Thou Ruler of the nations, we are thankful for leaders like Abraham Lincoln, whom Thou didst use to save our country in the hour of danger. Thou hast permitted us to become a great nation. But we, alas, are unworthy of Thy favor, for there is much crime and ungodliness in the land. Have mercy upon our people, O Lord, and lead them to repentance. Grant to each of us true sorrow for sin, but also faith and courage to resist temptation to do wrong. Help us to be sincere Christians and upright citizens. Give the President and all officials of State true wisdom. Move them to seek the welfare of the people at all times. Bless the schools and Sunday schools of America. Enable parents and teachers to guide the young in the way of obedience. We ask it in the name of Jesus, who loved us and gave Himself for us. Amen.

ON QUEEN VICTORIA DAY

Gracious God, we thank Thee on this day for rulers like Queen Victoria, who loved Thy Law and always had the welfare of the people at heart. In Thy mercy raise up in Canada and all other countries wise and good men who will punish the wicked and protect the righteous. Destroy the power of cruel men who shed innocent blood, who rob people of their freedom and make them slaves, who hate and persecute the Church. Cause sinners everywhere to repent of their sins and to turn to Thee in faith, and be pleased to send peace and plenty upon those who are poor and miserable. Lord, we thank and praise Thee for the many undeserved blessings we enjoy in this free land. May we show that we are truly thankful by learning and obeying Thy Word, and by inviting others to come and share in Thy grace and forgiveness. We ask this in the name of Jesus, who died for all. Amen.

ON DOMINION DAY

Eternal God, Ruler of the nations, as we celebrate Dominion Day, we thank Thee for having so guided the affairs of our country as to bring into existence a nation of peace-loving people from many lands. As we think of those countries where the people have lost their freedom and are ruled by wicked and cruel men, we realize how great Thy goodness and mercy have been toward us. We thank Thee, Lord, for the freedom we enjoy, and above all for the freedom of religion and the right to worship Thee in our churches. Enable us by Thy grace to live a holy and righteous life, to be loyal to our country, to our homes, and to Thee. Give us Godfearing rulers, and grant them wisdom to do those things which will bring peace and blessing to the people of this nation. We ask it in the name of Jesus, our Savior. Amen.

ON MEMORIAL DAY

Merciful God and Father, on this Memorial Day we pray Thee to comfort the hearts of those whose loved ones laid down their lives for their country on the field of battle. Help us to appreciate the freedom for which these men offered the supreme sacrifice. May we show our thankfulness to Thee for all the blessings we enjoy in this free land by living pure and righteous lives and by doing our duty as citizens of our country and as members of the Church. Bless our government. Destroy the power of those who would plunge the nations into war. Grant peace to our country and to the world. Help us to spread the Gospel everywhere and to gladden the hearts of sinners with the good news of Thy redeeming love. Hear us for Jesus' sake. Amen.

ON INDEPENDENCE DAY

Dear heavenly Father, as we celebrate Independence Day, we raise our hearts and voices in thanksgiving to Thee for the freedom we have enjoyed in the United States for so many years. Help us to walk in Thy commandments, to love Thee and our neighbor, and to set others an example of good citizenship from day to day. Protect us from wicked men who would overthrow our government and rob us of our freedom. Bless our country for the sake of the righteous who do Thy will. Help us to realize that we are in the world to serve Thee and to be a blessing to our fellow men and to our country. We ask it in Jesus' name. Amen.

PATRIOTIC, GENERAL

Eternal God, Lord of the nations, we acknowledge Thy great goodness in permitting us to live in a country in which the government does not interfere with religion, but permits each one to go to a church of his own choice. May we show that we are thankful for the blessing of religious freedom by diligently hearing and learning Thy Word and by bringing the good news of the Gospel to others. Help us to realize that we are Christian citizens and that as such we should pray for our rulers, keep the laws of the land, and set others a good example in holy living. Fill all civil rulers with wisdom and courage to do their duty and to seek the welfare of the people. And since Thou canst bless a nation only when the people are righteous, do Thou have mercy upon those who are living in sin, and lead them to repentance. Then shall the earth yield her increase, and God, even our own God, shall bless us. Hear our prayer, which we offer in Jesus' name. Amen.

84

IV. General Collects

1

Almighty God, our heavenly Father, who by Thy tender love towards us sinners hast given us Thy Son that, believing on Him, we might have everlasting life, grant us, we beseech Thee, Thy Holy Spirit, that we may continue steadfast in this faith and may come to everlasting life; through Jesus Christ, Thy Son, our Lord. Amen.

2

O almighty God, whom to know is everlasting life, grant us perfectly to know Thy Son, Jesus Christ, to be the Way, the Truth, and the Life, that, following His steps, we may steadfastly walk in the way that leadeth to eternal life; through the same Jesus Christ, Thy Son, our Lord. Amen.

3

Almighty and everlasting God, who hast willed that Thy Son should bear for us the pains of the cross that Thou mightest save us from the power of the devil, help us so to remember and give thanks for our Lord's suffering and death that we may obtain forgiveness of sins and everlasting life; through the same Jesus Christ, Thy Son, our Lord. Amen.

4

O Lord God, heavenly Father, we beseech Thee, let Thy Holy Spirit dwell in us that He may enlighten and lead us into all truth and evermore defend us from all temptations; through Jesus Christ, Thy Son, our Lord. Amen.

5

Grant to us, Lord, we beseech Thee, the Spirit to think and do always such things as are right, that we, who cannot do anything that is good without Thee, may by Thee be enabled to live according to Thy will; through Jesus Christ, Thy Son, our Lord, who liveth and reigneth with Thee and the Holy Spirit, ever one God, world without end. Amen.

6

O God, so rule and govern our hearts and minds by Thy Holy Spirit that, being ever mindful of the end of all things and the day of Thy just Judgment, we may be stirred up to holiness of living here and dwell with Thee forever hereafter; through Jesus Christ, Thy Son, our Lord, who liveth and reigneth with Thee and the Holy Spirit, ever one God, world without end. Amen.

7

Almighty God, our heavenly Father, whose mercies are new unto us every morning and who, though we have in no wise deserved Thy goodness, dost abundantly provide for all our wants of body and soul, give us, we pray Thee, Thy Holy Spirit that we may heartily acknowledge Thy merciful goodness toward us, give thanks for all Thy benefits, and serve Thee in willing obedience; through Jesus Christ, Thy Son, our Lord. Amen.

8

O Lord, we beseech Thee mercifully to receive the prayers of Thy people who call upon Thee; and grant that they may know what things they ought to do and also may have grace and power faithfully to fulfill the same; through Jesus Christ, Thy Son, our Lord, who liveth and reigneth with Thee and the Holy Spirit, ever one God, world without end. Amen.

9

Almighty and everlasting God, direct our actions according to Thy good pleasure, that in the name of Thy beloved Son we may be made to abound in good works; through the same Jesus Christ, Thy Son, our Lord. Amen.

10

Lord, we beseech Thee, grant Thy people grace to withstand the temptations of the devil and with pure hearts and minds to follow Thee, the only God; through Jesus Christ, Thy Son, our Lord, who liveth and reigneth with Thee and the Holy Spirit, ever one God, world without end. Amen.

11

God, who hast made Thine only-begotten Son the Savior of mankind and didst give Him the name of Jesus, mercifully grant that we who worship His name on earth may joyfully behold Him in heaven; through Jesus Christ, Thy Son, our Lord, who liveth and reigneth with Thee and the Holy Spirit, ever one God, world without end. Amen.

12

O Lord God, heavenly Father, from whom without ceasing we receive exceeding abundantly all good gifts and who daily of Thy pure grace guardest us against all evil, grant us, we beseech Thee, Thy Holy Spirit that, acknowledging with our whole heart all this Thy goodness, we may now and evermore thank and praise Thy loving-kindness and tender mercy; through Jesus Christ, Thy Son, our Lord. Amen.

V. Prayers for Private Use

MORNING PRAYERS

In the name of the Father and of the Son and of the Holy Ghost. Amen.

I thank Thee, my heavenly Father, through Jesus Christ, Thy dear Son, that Thou hast kept me this night from all harm and danger; and I pray Thee that Thou wouldst keep me this day also from sin and every evil, that all my doings and life may please Thee. For into Thy hands I commend myself, my body and soul, and all things. Let Thy holy angel be with me, that the wicked foe may have no power over me. Amen.

O help me, Lord, this day to be
Thy own dear child, and follow Thee;
And lead me, Savior, by Thy hand,
Until I reach the Heavenly Land. Amen.

Savior, I long to walk Closer with Thee;
Led by Thy guiding hand, Ever to be
Constantly near Thy side, Quickened and purified,
Living for Him who died Freely for me. Amen.

EVENING PRAYERS

In the name of the Father and of the Son and of the Holy Ghost. Amen.

I thank Thee, my heavenly Father, through Jesus Christ, Thy dear Son, that Thou hast graciously kept me this day; and I pray Thee that Thou wouldst forgive me all my sins where I have done wrong, and graciously keep me this night. For into Thy hands I commend myself, my body and soul, and all things. Let Thy holy angel be with me that the wicked foe may have no power over me. Amen.

Now the light has gone away;
Savior, listen while I pray,
Asking Thee to watch and keep
And to send me quiet sleep.

Jesus, Savior, wash away
All that has been wrong today;
Help me every day to be
Good and gentle, more like Thee.

Let my near and dear ones be
Always near and dear to Thee.
O bring me and all I love
To Thy happy home above. Amen.

FOR ASKING A BLESSING

Thou openest Thy hand, O Lord,
The earth is filled with good;
Teach us with thankful hearts to take
From Thee our daily food. Amen.

Great God, Thou Giver of all good,
Accept our praise, and bless our food,
Grace, health, and strength to us afford,
Through Jesus Christ, our blessed Lord. Amen.

Be present at our table, Lord;
Be here and everywhere adored.
Thy children bless, and grant that we
May feast in paradise with Thee. Amen.

Dear Lord, who doest all things good,
To whom the ravens look for food;
Be pleased to look on us from heaven,
And bless the food which Thou hast given. Amen.

The eyes of all wait upon Thee;
And Thou givest them their meat in due season.
Thou openest Thine hand,
And satisfiest the desire of every living thing.

Ps. 145:15, 16

We thank Thee, Lord, for our daily bread. May it strengthen and refresh our bodies. And we pray Thee, feed our souls with Thy heavenly grace, through Jesus Christ, our Lord. Amen.

We thank Thee, Lord God, heavenly Father, through Jesus Christ, our Lord, for all Thy benefits, who livest and reignest forever and ever. Amen.

FOR THE CONFESSION OF SINS

O almighty God, merciful Father, I, a poor, miserable sinner, confess unto Thee all my sins and iniquities with which I have ever offended Thee and justly deserved Thy temporal and eternal punishment. But I am heartily sorry for them and sincerely repent of them, and I pray Thee of Thy boundless mercy and for the sake of the holy, innocent, bitter sufferings and death of Thy beloved Son, Jesus Christ, to be gracious and merciful to me, a poor sinful being.

90

Indexes

TOPICAL INDEX

ALPHABETICAL INDEX *of* TUNES

METRICAL INDEX *of* TUNES

INDEX *of* FIRST LINES

TOPICAL INDEX

ALPHABETICAL INDEX *of* TUNES

Wie lieblich ist der Maien	99	Wir glauben all' an einen Gott	65
Wie schoen leuchtet	61	Wir pfluegen	100
Winchester New	238	Wo Gott zum Haus	29
Winchester Old	168, 183, 273	Woodworth	236
Winterton	174	Worcester	70

METRICAL INDEX *of* TUNES

S. M.

Energy	148, 187
Franconia	63
Marion (with refrain)	237
Potsdam	228
St. Michael	90
St. Thomas	116, 186
Schumann	170

S. M. D.

Diademata	122

C. M.

Antioch	9
Beatitudo	121
Bedford	151
Belmont	134
Chesterfield	1
Children's Praises (with refrain)	211
Clairvaux	128
Coronation	120
Cowper	231
Dundee	145, 153, 157
Evan	159
Horsley	43, 231
Little Ones	276
Lobt Gott, ihr Christen	12, 107
Martyrdom	36
St. Anne	235
St. Flavian	199, 219, 285
St. Peter	127, 163, 207
Spring Song	283
Tallis' Ordinal	246
Walder	155
Who Made the Sky	282
Winchester Old	168, 183, 273

C. M. D.

Bethlehem	152
Kingsfold	240

L. M.

Angelus	154
Die helle Sonn' leucht't	82
Duke Street	45, 196
Erhalt uns, Herr	74, 75, 165
Germany	149
Hamburg	42, 251
Herr Jesu Christ, dich	79 164
Hursley	254
Lasst uns erfreuen (with Alleluias)	50, 55, 242
Mendon	80, 171
O Heilige Dreifaltigkeit	81, 87
O Jesu Christ, mein's	195, 241
Old Hundredth	94, 106, 144
Pentecost	212
Puer nobis nascitur	3, 13
St. Crispin	136, 216, 236, 252
Tallis' Canon	95
Vom Himmel hoch	6, 11
Waltham	201
Winchester New	238
Wo Gott zum Haus	29
Woodworth	236

4. 4. 7. 4. 4. 7.

Ach Gott und Herr	58

5. 5. 7. 5. 5. 8.

Schoenster Herr Jesu	253

5. 5. 8. 8. 5. 5.

Seelenbraeutigam	184

6. 4. 6. 4.

Christmas Carol	295

6. 4. 6. 4. 6. 6. 6. 4.

Bethany	266
Heaven Is My Home	206
Winterton	174

6. 5. 6. 5.

Alle Jahre wieder	296
Eudoxia	98, 300
Naegeli	286
Offering	147
Perrine	182
St. Lucian	102

INDEX *of* FIRST LINES